BrightRED Study Guide

Curriculum for Excellence

N5

PRACTICAL WOODWORKING

David Horne

First published in 2018 by:
Bright Red Publishing Ltd
1 Torphichen Street
Edinburgh
EH3 8HX

A CIP record for this book is available from the British Library.

ISBN 978-1-906736-81-1

With thanks to: PDQ Digital Media Solutions Ltd. (layout), Dylan Hamilton (editorial)

Cover design and series book design by Caleb Rutherford – e i d e t i c.

Acknowledgements
Every effort has been made to seek all copyright-holders. If any have been overlooked, then Bright Red Publishing will be delighted to make the necessary arrangements.

Permission has been sought from all relevant copyright holders and Bright Red Publishing are grateful for the use of the following:

Images licensed by Ingram Image (pp 9, 10, 18, 20–24, 26, 30–31, 49, 50, 52, 60–61, 67 & 69); Caleb Rutherford – e i d e t i c (pp 10–11, 24–30, 32–34, 36–43, 45, 50, 52–60, 63, 64–5, 67–8, 73, 75, 77–8, 80–2, 83–4, 89, 91–3); Luke Milburn (CC BY 2.0)[1] (p 10); Etune (CC BY-SA 3.0)[2] (p 10); Primopiano/Shutterstock.com (p 18); Steve Bowbrick (CC BY 2.0)[1] (p 18); Werachai Sookruay (p 19); Ungvar/Shutterstock.com (p 19); qvist/Shutterstock.com (p 19); James Wellington (CC BY 2.0)[1] (p 19); Brodo (CC BY 3.0)[3] (p 19); William Murphy (CC BY-SA 2.0)[4] (p 19); Auri 98 (CC BY-SA 3.0)[2] (p 19); Fiberon (CC BY-ND 2.0)[5] (p 19); Corepics VOF/Shutterstock.com (p 20); Early spring/Shutterstock.com (pp 20 & 82); Searuss/Shutterstock.com (pp 20 & 91); pics721/Shutterstock.com (p 20); Lotus_studio/Shutterstock.com (p 20); Stephen Rees/Shutterstock.com (p 20); Trong Nguyen/Shutterstock.com (p 20); Lotus_studio/Shutterstock.com (p 20); Stephen Rees/Shutterstock.com (p 20); Das Ohr (CC BY-SA 3.0)[2] (p 21); charl898/Shutterstock.com (p 21); Coyau (CC BY-SA 3.0)[2] (p 21); Porsche-Makus (CC BY-SA 4.0)[6] (p 21); Davidzdh (CC BY-SA 4.0)[6] (p 21); Bystander (CC BY-SA 3.0)[2] (p 22); Design Trust for Public Space (CC BY 2.0)[1] (p 22); sergey0506/Shutterstock.com (pp 23 & 90); Rotor DB (CC BY-SA 3.0)[2] (p 22); Peter Vanco/Shutterstock.com (p 23); frooil/Shutterstock.com (p 23); Elke Wetzig (CC BY-SA 3.0)[2] (p 23); Arkadiusz Zarzecki (CC BY-SA 3.0)[2] (p 27); Za (CC BY-SA 3.0)[2] (pp 32–3); Jameslwoodward (CC BY-SA 3.0)[2] (p 39); Jomegat (CC BY-SA 2.5)[7] (p 40); Peter sjogren (CC BY 3.0)[3] (p 40); Simon A. Eugster (CC BY-SA 3.0)[2] (pp 41 & 86); YK/Shutterstock.com (p 42); Dima Moroz/Shutterstock.com (p 46); Africa Studio/Shutterstock.com (p 46); Zephyris (CC BY-SA 3.0)[2] (p 48); bkrpr (CC BY-SA 2.0)[4] (p 49); theerapol sri-in/Shutterstock.com (p 50); Scott Atkins (p 51); Domiriat (CC BY-SA 4.0)[6] (p 52); Glenn McKechnie (CC BY-SA 3.0)[2] (p 54); Jordanhill School D&T Dept (CC BY 2.0)[1] (p 54); Glenn McKechniederivative (CC BY-SA 3.0)[2] (p 56); Emilian Robert Vicol (CC BY 2.0)[1] (p 57); Graibeard (CC BY-SA 2.0)[4] (p 57); Greg Hume (CC BY-SA 3.0)[2] (pp 60 & 77); Charles & Hudson (CC BY-SA 2.0)[4] (p 60); Santeri Viinamäki (CC BY-SA 4.0)[6] (p 60); Tsungam (CC BY-SA 4.0)[6] (pp 61 & 78); Mark Hunter (CC BY 2.0)[1] (p 61); Luigi Zanasi (CC BY-SA 2.0 CA)[8] (p 61); Simon A. Eugster (CC BY-SA 3.0)[2] (pp 62–3); Duncan Hull (CC BY 2.0)[1] (p 64); Daniel Gilbey Photography – My portfolio/Shutterstock.com (p 64); Ilike/Shutterstock.com (p 64); VictorH11/Shutterstock.com (p 64); Bennyartist/Shutterstock.com (p 65); Laurent Renault/Shutterstock.com (p 65); Anson0618/Shutterstock.com (p 65); Johan (CC BY-SA 3.0)[2] (p 65); yavuzunlu/Shutterstock.com (p 66); Safety signs © Freesignage UK (www.online-sign.com) (p 66); Lilly_M (CC BY-SA 3.0)[2] (p 66); KOchstudiO (CC BY-SA 3.0)[2] (p 67); g-stockstudio/Shutterstock.com (p 68); Phovoir/Shutterstock.com (p 69); Rowan Peter (CC BY-SA 2.0)[4] (p 69); Wicker Paradise (CC BY 2.0)[1] (p 69); Kriengsuk Prasroetsung/Shutterstock.com (p 74); Emrys2 (CC BY-SA 3.0)[2] (p 81); Vadym Andrushchenko/Shutterstock.com (p 90).

[1] (CC BY 2.0) https://creativecommons.org/licenses/by/2.0/
[2] (CC BY-SA 3.0) https://creativecommons.org/licenses/by-sa/3.0/
[3] (CC BY 3.0) https://creativecommons.org/licenses/by/3.0/
[4] (CC BY-SA 2.0) https://creativecommons.org/licenses/by-sa/2.0/
[5] (CC BY-ND 2.0) https://creativecommons.org/licenses/by-nd/2.0/
[6] (CC BY-SA 4.0) https://creativecommons.org/licenses/by-sa/4.0/
[7] (CC BY-SA 2.5) https://creativecommons.org/licenses/by-sa/2.5/
[8] (CC BY-SA 2.0 CA) https://creativecommons.org/licenses/by-sa/2.0/ca/

Printed and bound in the UK.

MIX
Paper from responsible sources
FSC® C013254

CONTENTS

INTRODUCING NATIONAL 5 PRACTICAL WOODWORKING

INTRODUCTION TO THE COURSE

COURSE CONTENT

National 5 Practical Woodworking is largely workshop-based, combining elements of theory and practical woodworking techniques. Throughout the course, as well as learning how to use a range of tools, equipment and materials safely, you will also develop skills in reading drawings and diagrams, measuring and marking out, cutting, shaping and finishing materials.

This course develops skills in three main areas. Each area provides opportunities for you to understand safe working practices, sustainability issues, and good practice in recycling within a workshop environment. Each area of study covers a different set of woodworking skills. All areas include skills and associated knowledge in measuring, marking out, cutting and jointing techniques.

(SQA, National 5 Course Specification Practical Woodworking version 2.0, p2 and p4, https://www.sqa.org.uk/files_ccc/PracticalWoodworkingCourseSpecN5.pdf)

SKILLS, KNOWLEDGE AND UNDERSTANDING FOR THE COURSE

The following provides a broad overview of the subject skills, knowledge and understanding you will develop during the course:

- Using a range of woodworking tools, equipment and materials safely and correctly for woodworking tasks with some complex features.

- Adjusting tools where necessary, following safe practices.

- Reading and interpreting drawings and diagrams in familiar and some unfamiliar contexts.

- Measuring and marking out timber sections and sheet materials in preparation for cutting and shaping tasks with some complex features.

- Practical creativity in the context of simple and familiar woodworking tasks with some complex features.

- Following, with autonomy, given stages of a practical problem-solving approach to woodworking tasks.

- Applying knowledge and understanding of safe working practices in a workshop environment.

- Applying knowledge and understanding of the properties and uses of a range of woodworking materials.

- Applying knowledge and understanding of sustainability issues in a practical woodworking context.

COURSE ASSESSMENT STRUCTURE

The course assessment is split into two main sections, the question paper and the practical activity. The question paper is out of 60 marks, which is scaled to represent 30% of the overall marks for the course assessment, with the practical activity having 70 marks allocated to it to represent the remaining 70%.

Question paper

The question paper will give you an opportunity to demonstrate the skills, knowledge and understanding you have learned while working through the practical woodworking course content. In the question paper, you can expect to find questions relating to the following topics:

- Measuring and marking tools
- Reading and interpreting drawings
- Materials
- Bench work
- Flat-frame construction and assembly
- Carcase construction and assembly
- Use and care of machines and power tools
- Surface preparation and finish
- Health and safety
- Sustainability and recycling

Practical activity

The practical activity will allow you to demonstrate the application of skills and knowledge developed during the course to produce a finished product to a given standard and specification.

The practical activity will be to manufacture a product and complete a log book. The log book will be provided as part of the assessment task.

Marks are awarded for:

- Log book
- Flat-frame construction
- Carcase construction
- Machining/turnery
- Finishing
- Overall assembly

The practical activity will give you an opportunity to demonstrate the following skills, knowledge and understanding:

- Selecting and using a range of woodworking tools, equipment, materials and finishes.
- Reading, interpreting and following given working drawings, outline specification information and cutting lists.
- Marking out, cutting and shaping component parts.
- Manufacturing a finished product to given drawing standards.
- Working and using tools and equipment in accordance with recognised procedures and safe working practices.

More information can be found on the question paper and the practical activity on pp. 70–71 of this book.

 THINGS TO DO AND THINK ABOUT

Success in the Practical Woodworking course can allow you to progress on to many exciting and enjoyable courses and professions. Use the internet to research the following jobs: joiner, plumber, electrician, architect and engineer.

COURSE ASSESSMENT

COURSE ASSESSMENT CHECKLIST

In the exam for National 5 Practical Woodworking, you could be asked to demonstrate a knowledge and understanding of a huge range of materials, jointing techniques, tools and machines. This section provides you with a handy list of all the tools and machines that you will have to be able to either identify or describe their use.

Measuring and marking out tools

- Steel rule
- Tape measure
- Try square
- Marking gauge
- Mortise gauge
- Cutting gauge
- Sliding bevel
- Marking knife
- Templates
- Dovetail template
- Outside calipers

Bench work

- Bench vice
- Saws:
  - Tenon saw
  - Coping saw
  - Rip saw
  - Cross-cut saw
  - Panel saw
- Chisels:
  - Bevel edge chisel
  - Firmer chisel
  - Mortise chisel
- Mallet
- Hammers:
  - Cross pein hammer
  - Claw hammer
- Pincers
- Planes:
  - Jack plane
  - Smoothing plane
  - Plough plane
  - Rebate plane
  - Combination plane
  - Block plane
  - Bull-nose plane
- Spoke shave
- Hand router
- Hand drill
- Hand brace
- Bradawl
- Nail punch
- Screwdrivers:
  - Straight
  - Cross head

Cramping

- Cramps:
  - Sash cramp
  - G cramp
  - Mitre cramp
  - Band cramp
  - Sting and block

Mechanical fixings and adhesives

- Nails:
  - Round
  - Oval brads
  - Panel pins
- Screws:
  - Round/dome head
  - Countersink
  - Slotted head
  - Cross head
- Angle brackets
- Corner brackets
- Knock down fittings
- Adhesives: interior and exterior

Machines and power tools

- Woodturning lathe: faceplate and turning between centres
- Lathe tools:
  - Forked/butterfly centre
  - Dead centre
  - Revolving centre
  - Gouge   o Parting chisel
  - Scraper   o Skew chisel
- Parts of the lathe:
  - Bed
  - Headstock
  - Tailstock
  - Tool rest
- Belt sander
- Disc sander
- Pillar/pedestal drill

contd

- Drill bits:
  - Twist drill
  - Countersink rose
  - Flat bit
  - Forstner bit
- Mortise machine

- Power tools:
  - Drills: corded and cordless
  - Sanders: orbital and belt
  - Cordless screwdriver
  - Jig saw

Surface preparation and finishing techniques

- Abrasive types:
  - Glass paper
  - Garnet paper
- Abrasive grades: fine, medium and course

- Finishes:
  - Varnish
  - Stain
  - Wax
  - Oil: Danish, linseed and vegetable

Safe working practices

- Personal protective equipment:
  - Apron
  - Gloves
  - Safety goggles
  - Safety specs
  - Visors
  - Dust protection

MATERIALS AND JOINTING TECHNIQUES CHECKLIST

Materials

- Softwood:
  - White Pine
  - Red Pine
  - Cedar
  - Larch

- Hardwood:
  - Ash
  - Oak
  - Beech
  - Mahogany
  - Meranti

- Manufactured Board:
  - Chipboard
  - Plywood
  - Hardboard
  - MDF
  - Blockboard

Jointing techniques

- Flat frame:
  - Butt joint
  - Mitre joint
  - Dowel joint
  - Corner-halving joint
  - Bridle joint
  - Haunched mortise and tenon joint
  - Stub mortise and tenon joint
  - Through mortise and tenon joint
  - T-halving joint
  - Dovetail-halving joint
  - Cross-halving joint

- Carcase construction:
  - Butt joint
  - Corner rebate joint
  - Through housing joint
  - Stopped housing joint
  - Dowel joint

READING AND INTERPRETING DRAWINGS AND DOCUMENTS CHECKLIST

- Working drawings
- Pictorial drawings
- Cutting lists
- Orthographic projection
- Scale

- Basic drawing conventions:
  - Line types
  - Outlines
  - Centre lines
  - Hidden detail lines

- Dimension lines:
  - Linear
  - Radial
  - Angular (45°)
  - Diametric dimensions

MEASUREMENT AND TOLERANCES

UNIT OF MEASUREMENT

The unit of measurement used in Practical Woodworking is **millimetres** (mm). It is essential that millimetres are used rather than centimetres as millimetres are a more accurate unit of measurement. The sizes in the working drawings you will be using to make your models throughout the course will be stated in millimetres.

DATUM EDGE

When marking out on wood, measurements should be taken from a datum. A **datum edge** is a flat or straight edge from which all measurements should be taken, otherwise you're in danger of making cumulative errors.

The face edge should be carefully chosen, making sure it is flat with a straight edge, then it is marked with a small symbol for identification purposes. A face side is then selected which is at right angles to the face edge. All measurements are then taken from this side and/or edge. It is also important to remember that while using a try square and marking gauge, you should always make sure that the stock of each tool is continuously pressed against either the face side or face edge.

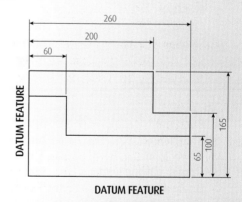

DATUM FEATURE

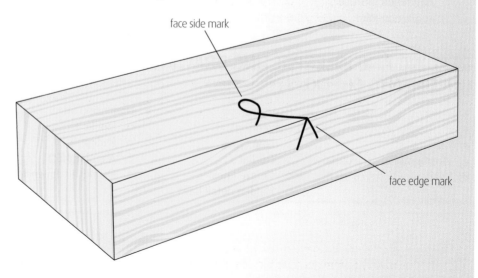

face side mark

face edge mark

WORKING TO TOLERANCE

In the case of Practical Woodworking, the **tolerance** of a component is the permissible amount of variation to the size given in a working drawing or a gap between a joint. The tolerance that you will be expected to work to for National 5 is ± 1mm (plus or minus 1mm). Working to this tolerance will ensure that different parts of your model fit together correctly and that the final model looks good. The types of tasks you will have to do to this given tolerance are marking out, planing, drilling to a given position, sanding to a line and making sure that any gaps between joints don't exceed 1mm.

MEASURING TOOLS

Throughout the course in Practical Woodworking you will need to show a good degree of accuracy and skill in using the following measuring and marking out tools: steel rule, tape measure, outside callipers, try square, marking knife, sliding bevel, templates, a dovetail template, marking gauge, mortise gauge and a cutting gauge.

Steel Rule

The steel rule is available in a variety of lengths, e.g. 150mm, 300mm, 500mm and 1m. The most common one used in a school workshop is the 300mm. Steel rules are used when measurements must be accurate.

The graduations which are machined into the rule start at the **zero end**, which enables gauge setting and allows you to measure accurately from a corner or surface. A steel rule can also be used for testing surfaces for flatness.

Tape Measure

The tape measure is used to measure longer material sizes. The blade is made from flexible steel with graduations marked onto it which retracts back into the case when released. There will be a label on the case to indicate the length of the blade (usually 3m or 5m) and the length of the case itself (e.g. 70mm). The case length is needed when an internal measurement is being taken; for example, if the distance on tape is 430mm, the total inside measurement is actually 500mm.

Outside Calipers

Outside calipers are used to check the outside diameter of cylindrical objects. An example of where you may use outside calipers is after you have parallel turned your wood down on a wood lathe, and you wish to check that you have achieved the required diameter uniformly across the distance specified on your template or working drawing.

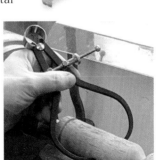

Outside callipers

Outside callipers being used to check the diameter of the turned wooden blank while it's still on the wood lathe

THINGS TO DO AND THINK ABOUT

1. Why is it important to take dimensions from a datum edge?
2. Why is it necessary to remember to include the length of the case of the tape measure while taking an internal measurement?
3. To what tolerance must your marking out be to ensure you achieve a pass at National 5?
4. Give two reasons why you should work to a tolerance.
5. State the purpose of outside calipers.

MARKING OUT TOOLS

MARKING OUT ANGLES AND SHAPES

Try Square

The try square is used to check and mark **right angles** (90°) on wood. It has three main parts, which are labelled (left). The blade is made from steel, the stock from wood or plastic with a brass wear plate attached to it to ensure minimum wear. It is the length of the blade which the range of sizes are based on. They are available in sizes from 100mm to 300mm.

Where lines are required across the grain you could use a **marking knife** to score the fibres of the wood. This will make sawing or chiselling along the line easier. Although using a marking knife is more accurate than using a pencil, care should be taken as a score mark made by a marking knife is not easily removed if a mistake is made.

ONLINE

Check out the link at www.brightredbooks.net to find out how to check your square's squareness.

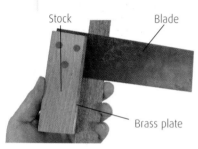

Stock   Blade

Brass plate

Marking knife

Try square being used to check a flat frame is square

Stock held tight against the edge of the wood

Marking knife in use

Sliding Bevel

The sliding bevel allows you to set any angles from 0° to 180°. Sliding bevels have a wooden stock and a blade made from steel. It is commonly used to mark out dovetail or mitre joints.

Templates

If you need to mark out the same shape a number of times, particularly an irregular shape, it is a good idea to make a **template** to draw around. You can make a template out of any thin scrap material such as card, plywood, aluminium or plastic. The type of material chosen for a template is determined by the number of times it is to be used. A steel template will be much more robust than one made of card. The advantage of using a template is that once it is made you are able to repeatedly draw the same shape quickly and accurately.

A dovetail joint is a very complex joint to make which can take a long time to mark out. It is not uncommon to use a **dovetail template** like the one pictured. Not only is it quicker to mark out the dovetail joint, the chance of making an error while marking out the repetitive pattern of the dovetail joint will be reduced.

DON'T FORGET

The knife score must be made along a suitable straight edge, usually a try square.

DON'T FORGET

For assessment purposes, you should retain any templates you make.

A plastic template being used

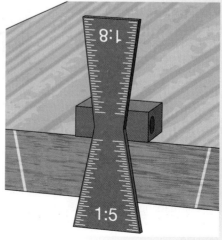

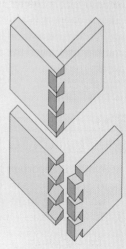

MARKING OUT PARALLEL LINES

Marking Gauge

The marking gauge is used to mark a line parallel to an edge or side along the **grain** of a piece of wood. Lines parallel to an edge are useful when you want to cut material to a certain depth or width, cut off strips or mark a number of holes all in line.

The marking gauge is made up of four main parts, the stem, stock, spur and thumbscrew. To set the distance between the moveable stock and the fixed spur, which is attacked to the stem, you adjust the thumbscrew.

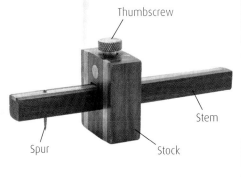

Thumbscrew

Stem

Spur   Stock

When setting the marking gauge, make sure the zero end of the steel rule is flat on the stock with the point of the spur touching the steel rule

If it's necessary to make slight adjustments to the distance set, you can tap either end of the stem up or down against the workbench

Marking gauge in use. Make sure you keep the stock of the marking gauge tight against the wood

The gauge is one of the more difficult marking tools to use and will take some practice. The trick to leaving a straight groove along the grain is to make sure you keep the stock tight against the side of the wood then lightly push it away from you. Make sure you trail the spur along the wood: do not have the spur so vertical that it tends to dig into the wood.

Mortise Gauge

The mortise gauge is similar to a marking gauge but it has two spurs, one which is fixed to the stem and the other which is adjustable. A mortise gauge is used to mark out two parallel lines which are set for the desired thickness of mortises and tenons.

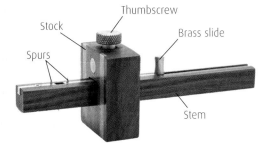

Stock   Thumbscrew

Brass slide

Spurs

Stem

Cutting Gauge

Again, the cutting gauge is similar to the marking gauge but it has a knife blade fixed to the stem instead of a spur. A cutting gauge is used to cut across the grain parallel to the end of a piece of wood which will make it easier and neater to cut across with a saw.

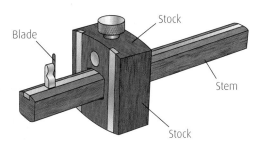

Blade

Stock

Stem

Stock

DON'T FORGET

If it's necessary to make slight adjustments to the distance set, you can tap either end of the stem up or down against the workbench.

DON'T FORGET

To make gauging easier, you can hold the wood in the vice or against a bench hook/ sawing board.

DON'T FORGET

If you lean too heavily while pushing the marking gauge away from you, you will end up with a wavy line. If necessary, go over the line several times rather than trying to get a deep line in one.

 THINGS TO DO AND THINK ABOUT

1. Draw and label the different parts of a try square then say what its uses are.

2. Explain the reason for creating a template to mark out certain shapes.

3. State what would influence your choice of material for a template.

4. Explain the main differences between the marking gauge, mortise gauge and the cutting gauge.

ONLINE TEST

Head to www.brightredbooks.net to test yourself on marking out tools.

DRAWING CONVENTIONS

ONLINE

Find out more about the basic drawing conventions by following the link on the Digital Zone.

Outline

The outline, shown as a thick continuous line, is used to signify visible edges and outlines of an object.

Hidden detail line

The hidden detail line, shown as a dashed thin line, is used to signify hidden detail in a drawing, for example, to show something that is there but which you can't see from that particular view point.

Centre line

The centre line, shown as a long dash–dot chain line, is used to signify centres of symmetry, for example, the centre of a circle or an arc in an object.

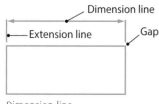

Dimension line

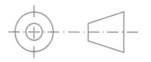

3rd angle projection symbol

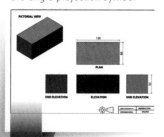

BASIC DRAWING CONVENTIONS

As you work through the Practical Woodworking course, you will be issued with various working drawings and you will be expected to interpret these drawings and be able to pick out relevant information needed to manufacture a model. Working drawings are used extensively by various professionals from joiners, plumbers and electricians to engineers and architects.

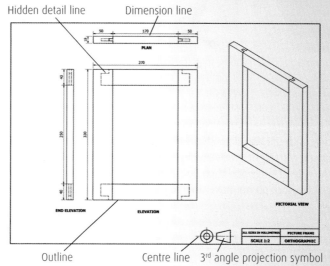

Working drawing for a picture frame

In order that everyone who needs to use a working drawing is able to interpret the drawing and pick out the relevant information needed, all working drawings are done according to a set of rules set out by the British Standards Institute (BSI). The set of rules are known as drawing conventions. The purpose of this chapter is to introduce you to the BSI drawing conventions used in working drawings, and to enable you to understand what the various conventions that have been used in the drawings represent, and what information you would expect to find in a working drawing.

First, you will find that there are a variety of line types in use and they all mean something different. The four main line types that you will find in a working drawing are outlines, centre lines, hidden detail lines and dimension lines. Each of the line types and what they represent are shown.

The dimension line is shown as a thin continuous line with solid arrow heads at either end. The points of the arrows should be touching each extension line. There should be a small gap between the object being dimensioned and the extension line. The actual size of the part of the object being dimensioned should sit centrally, just above the dimension line as shown.

An example of the four main line types in use can be found in the working drawing for a picture frame shown.

Another feature of a working drawing is the way it is laid out. This is another drawing convention used to ensure that all working drawings are laid out in a standardised way. The 3rd angle projection symbol (shown left) is used to indicate the order in which the different views of the object are laid out. For example, the front view, called the elevation, is placed under the plan view, which is the view of the picture frame looking at it from above.

An example of a basic orthographic drawing is shown (left).

DIMENSIONS

Dimensions on a working drawing signify the actual size of a part of an object. All sizes shown will be in millimetres unless it is stated otherwise. Millimetres are used as that is the degree of accuracy required in wood work. A working drawing will include measurements to indicate the sizes of individual parts and the overall length, breadth and thickness of the assembled object. The four main dimension types that you will find in a working drawing are linear, radial, angular and diametric dimensions. Each of the methods of dimensioning and what they represent are shown below.

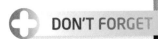
DON'T FORGET

Sizes are always shown in millimetres unless otherwise stated.

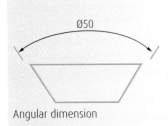

Linear dimension

A linear dimension is used to show the size of an object in one dimension only, for example, the length or width of the object.

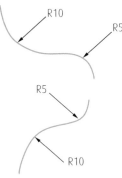

Radial dimension

When an object has a curve, an arc or a rounded corner to be created, you will be given a radial dimension. If a radial dimension is required, an R before the number denotes the radius.

An angular dimension, like the example shown, is used to show the angle a part is to be either cut or shaped to. The most common place you will find an angular dimension is on a mitre joint where you are required to cut a joint to 45°.

An example of the four main dimensioning types in use can be seen in the working drawing shown below.

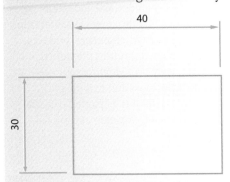

Angular dimension

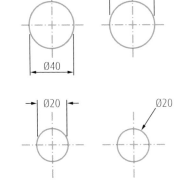

Diametric dimension

Diametric dimensions, like the examples shown, are used to show the size of a hole that is to be either cut or drilled out. A dimension showing a diameter of a circle will always have the symbol Ø before the number.

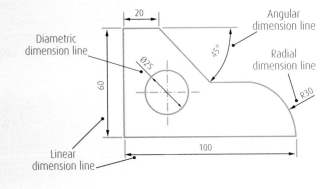

Diametric dimension line

Angular dimension line

Radial dimension line

Linear dimension line

 THINGS TO DO AND THINK ABOUT

1. The following different line types can be found in a working drawing: outline; hidden detail line; centre line; dimension line.
    Sketch each line type and state its purpose.

2. Sketch an example of the following dimension techniques found in a working drawing: linear dimension; radial dimension; diametric dimension; angular dimension.

ONLINE TEST

Test yourself on reading and interpreting drawings at www.brightredbooks.net

WORKING DRAWINGS AND CUTTING LISTS

WORKING DRAWINGS

The primary purpose of the working drawings you will be given as you work through the various models in Practical Woodworking is to provide you with all the information you need to make all the component parts, and to show you how each of those individual parts will be joined together. Working drawings tend to be produced by designers, architects or CAD technicians and then passed on to other professionals such as engineers, builders and joiners to read and work from. With this in mind, they have to present the information in such a way that it eliminates confusion. To achieve this, they provide the required information in a variety of formats such as orthographic drawings of individual parts and assemblies, pictorial drawings of individual parts and assemblies, exploded pictorial drawings and scaled detail drawings. They would also include a completed cutting list.

An example of each will be shown throughout this chapter.

PARTS OF A WORKING DRAWING

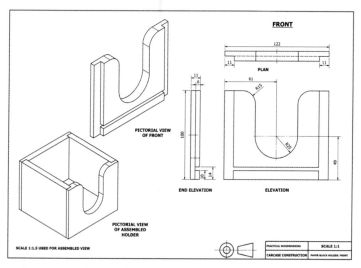

Working drawing for an individual part

Individual parts

The working drawing shown is for an individual part of a paper block holder. To aid clarity for the person who will be reading and working from the working drawing, the designer has provided an orthographic drawing of the part, a pictorial drawing of the part, and an assembled view of the completed model to help show how the specific part fits into the completed model.

Assembled and exploded parts

In the working drawing shown below, the designer has provided an assembled orthographic view with the overall sizes of a picture frame. To help add clarity to how the picture frame will look when it's assembled, an assembled pictorial view has also been provided.

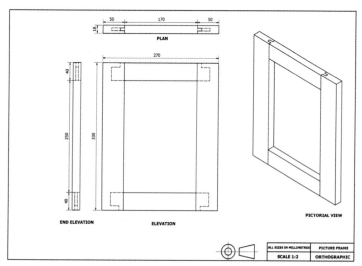

Working drawing of an assembly

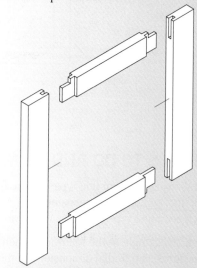

Exploded pictorial drawing of the picture frame

contd

In the example shown, you will see the designer of the picture frame has provided hidden detail lines in the orthographic view to help show how the rails of the frame are joined to stiles. This information could also have been shown by including an exploded pictorial view. An example of an exploded pictorial view of the picture frame is shown.

Drawn to scale

Working drawings are drawn to scale and the scale used will be indicated on the drawing. The scale used by the designer will depend on either the actual size of the original product or the level of detail that is required to be shown. For example, if the product has been drawn to its actual size, it has been drawn to a scale of 1:1; however, if the designer needed to show an intricate detail of a part, they may increase the scale used to perhaps 2:1, which would make the drawing twice as large as the actual size.

In this case, the designer has decided to use a complex woodworking joint, a haunched mortise and tenon, to join the rails of the frame to the stiles. Due to this joint having some intricate parts, the designer included a scaled drawing of that joint to help the person who is making the joint have a clearer idea of what they want made.

Cutting lists

A cutting list is an integral part of any working drawing. It includes an accurate, itemised list of all the individual parts that are required in the manufacture of a product.

You could expect to find the following information on a cutting list:

- The names of the various parts required in the model.
- The number required of each part.
- The material each part is to be made from.
- The specific dimensions each part must be cut to.
- The name of the model the cutting list has been produced for.

As you can see from the example, a typical cutting list is divided into several different columns and rows to convey this information in a clear and easy to understand format.

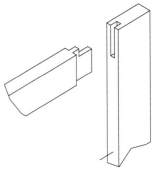

Scaled exploded pictorial drawing of a haunched mortise and tenon joint

Cutting list					
Project: Picture frame					
Part	**Number required**	**Material**	**Dimensions (mm)**		
			Length	**Breadth**	**Thickness**
Stile	2	Mahogany	330	50	18
Rail	2	Mahogany	230	40	18
Base	1	Plywood	270	190	3

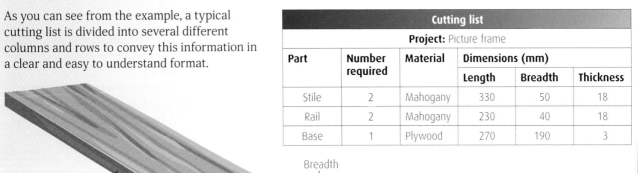

Breadth

Length

Thickness

The positions of the length, breadth and thickness of a strip of wood are labelled above

THINGS TO DO AND THINK ABOUT

1. State the name of two professions who read and work from working drawings.

2. Describe three methods a designer uses to help improve the clarity of a working drawing.

3. State two factors that will influence the choice of scale used in a working drawing.

4. State what the term scale 2:1 means.

5. Other than the dimensions of the component parts, state two pieces of information you would expect to find on a cutting list.

WORKING PROPERTIES AND DEFECTS IN WOOD

As part of the Practical Woodworking course, at National 5 level you are expected to be able to give accurate information in terms of the working properties and appearance of a variety of softwoods, hardwoods and manufactured boards. The working properties and appearance of the wide range of softwoods, hardwoods and manufactured boards are dependent on which tree the wood comes from and, in the case of manufactured board, how it's been made. Understanding the range of properties will help you select the most appropriate material for the job in hand.

ONLINE

Check out the timber durability chart on the Digital Zone.

WORKING PROPERTIES

The main characteristics to consider are:

- **Weight/density:** this can vary considerably, but generally hardwoods tend to be heavier than softwoods. Exceptions include balsa, a very lightweight hardwood and yew, a heavy softwood.

- **Strength:** the strength of wood is determined by its density. This is the wood's ability to withstand a force without breaking or bending.

- **Hardness:** the ability of a material to resist wear, scratching and indentation.

- **Ease of working:** how a material behaves when worked by hand or machine tools. Hardwoods are generally more difficult to work with; however, a particularly knotty softwood, like pine, can cause even an experienced carpenter difficulty when working with a hard knot.

- **Durability and resistance to decay:** this is the ability of a material to withstand wear, especially as a result of weathering. Durability should be considered if the product is liable to be used in damp situations such as a bathroom or kitchen, or if it will be used outside. The durability of a product can be improved by applying a finish to protect the wood from rot and decay. You should expect a wood that is described as being durable to last around 15 years in damp conditions. In general, hardwoods tend to be more durable and rot-resistant.

- **Appearance and grain structure:** softwoods tend be mainly pale in colour and have a more open grain compared to the wide variety of colourful (light to dark colours), close-grained hardwoods that are commercially available.

- **Cost and availability:** due to the length of time hardwoods take to grow to full maturity (around 100 years), they are considerably more expensive to buy than softwoods. Softwoods are faster growing, taking around 30 years to reach full maturity. Manufactured board is the cheapest of all.

DON'T FORGET

Before you begin to mark out your wood, you should check for defects such as knots, and decide if there is any way you can avoid cutting a joint directly on an area of the wood which has a knot.

DEFECTS IN NATURAL TIMBER

Timber is prone to defects which can cause some difficulties when it is being worked. Common defects to be aware of include **knots**, **warping** and **splits**.

Knots

Knots weaken the timber and, due to them being particularly hard, they can cause problems when using hand and machine tools.

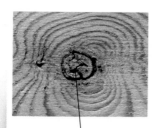

Example of a **knot** on a piece of softwood

contd

Warping

Bowing, cupping and twisting are all ways in which timber can warp. **Warping** is the general name given to any distortion from the true shape of the timber.

Bowing: a curve along the length of the face of a board.

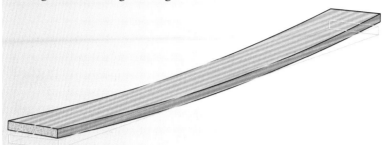

Bowing, view from the top

Cupping: a curve across the width of the face of a board.

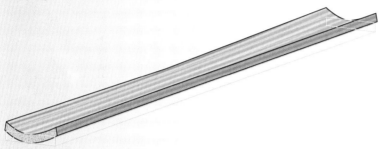

Cupping, pictorial view from the top

Twisting and winding: a board that is curved like a propeller.

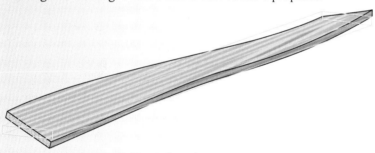

Twisting and winding, pictorial view from the top

Splits

The evaporation of moisture is greater at the ends of boards than elsewhere, thus end splits are very common in natural seasoned timber. The ends of boards should be protected in some way, such as painting end grain, as splits will weaken the structure of the timber and spoil its appearance.

THINGS TO DO AND THINK ABOUT

1. Which property should be considered if the product you are making will be used outside?

2. Suggest how the durability of a product can be improved to protect the wood from rot and decay.

3. Describe how a knot in a wood can be difficult to work with and suggest a possible solution to avoiding cutting a joint directly on a piece of wood which has a knot.

4. Warping is the general name given to any distortion from the true shape of the timber. Name and sketch the four different types of warping.

VIDEO LINK

Find out more about defects in wood by watching the video at www.brightredbooks.net

VIDEO LINK

Check out the clip on the Digital Zone to learn about the artificial seasoning of wood.

ONLINE TEST

Test yourself on the working properties and appearance of wood at www.brightredbooks.net

SOFTWOODS

Scots pine: an example of the tall and slender shape of a softwood tree

Example of the mushroom shape of a hardwood tree, in this case an oak

Example of the grain of a softwood

Oak grain: an example of the grain of a hardwood

ONLINE

Follow the link on the Digital Zone for a wood database.

INTRODUCTION TO WOOD

Types of Wood

Wood can be bought as either natural timber (solid wood) or manufactured board (plywood, blockboard).

Natural timber is either hardwood or softwood depending on which type of tree it comes from. Hardwoods come from broadleaved deciduous trees which lose their leaves in autumn and grow in the familiar mushroom shape. Some common hardwoods are oak, mahogany and beech.

Softwoods come from coniferous (cone-bearing) trees which are sometimes known as evergreens. They normally grow tall and slender and keep their needle-like leaves throughout the year. Common softwoods are pine, cedar and larch.

Hardwood trees normally take around 100–150 years to grow to full maturity while the faster growing softwood trees only take around 30 years to grow to full maturity, although both can live in the wild for many years longer. This makes hardwood more expensive. It also looks more attractive for furniture than softwoods.

It is wrong to think that a softwood will be soft and a hardwood will be hard. In fact, Balsa wood, which is a hardwood, is one of the softest woods available. Softwoods are usually lighter in weight, lighter in colour, and are more easily worked than many of the hardwoods.

The requirements for National 5 state that you should be able to name, identify, suggest the approximate cost and the possible uses of four softwoods, five hardwoods and five manufactured boards. You should also be able to describe the working properties of softwood/hardwood/manufactured boards in terms of their strength, durability and ease of working/cutting/shaping. The following provides all the information you need to know.

Pine cone and branch

Types of leaves found on hardwood trees

SOFTWOOD

Red Pine

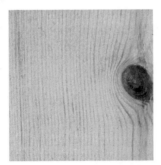

Cost: Inexpensive

Working properties: A very durable, strong material that glues and finishes well. It is easy to work with using both hand and machine tools. A disadvantage of red pine is it can be quite knotty and prone to warping.

Typical uses: Used in the building industry for floorboards, roof rafters, joists, roof trusses, children's toys, utility poles, and woodpulp for making paper.

Some examples of its uses are shown here.

contd

White Pine

Cost: Inexpensive

Working properties: A strong material which is reasonably durable, although it is better suited to interior use. It is easy to work with both by hand and machine tools. It also glues and finishes well.

Typical uses: Crates, boxes, wooden matchsticks, roof rafters, carving and woodpulp.

Some examples of its uses are shown here.

DON'T FORGET

It is wrong to think that a softwood will be soft and a hardwood will be hard. In fact, Balsa wood, which is a hardwood, is one of the softest woods available.

Western Red Cedar

Cost: Expensive

Working properties: Quite soft and lightweight, very durable making it well suited to outdoor constructions. Reddish orange with a straight grain that is knot-free.

Typical uses: Used outside for garden sheds, quality fencing, outdoor furniture, exterior walls and cladding.

Some examples of its uses are shown here.

Larch

Cost: Quite expensive

Working properties: It's strong and widely regarded as the most hard wearing, durable softwood. Most hand tool and machine operations produce good results. However, natural resins in the wood have a tendency to gum up saw blades.

Typical uses: Veneers, utility poles, fence posts, flooring, decking, boatbuilding and in the building industry.

Some examples of its uses are shown here.

ONLINE

Go to the Digital Zone for videos, tests, links and more.

THINGS TO DO AND THINK ABOUT

1. Natural timber is either hardwood or softwood depending on which type of tree it comes from. Describe the differences between the two tree types. You should compare the differences in their tree shape, leaf type and how long each tree takes to reach full maturity.

2. Name a disadvantage of Red pine.

3. Of the two types of Pine, which one is better suited to interior use?

4. List three typical uses for Red pine, White pine, Western red cedar and Larch.

HARDWOODS

ASH

Cost: Inexpensive

Working properties: A strong, hard, non-durable timber with good bending properties. It is easy to work with using both hand and machine tools and takes a finish well. Ash is pale brown in colour with a straight grain.

Typical uses: Hockey sticks, cricket and baseball bats, hammer handles and other turned objects such as garden tool handles.

Some examples of its uses are shown here.

VIDEO LINK

Do you know your ash from your oak? Find out at www.brightredbooks.net

OAK

Cost: Expensive

Working properties: Oak is a very strong, very durable, heavy and hard timber which responds well to steam-bending. It also glues, stains and finishes well. Most hand tool and machine operations produce good results. Oak is golden brown in colour with a highly figured grain.

Typical uses: High quality indoor furniture, garden furniture, flooring, wine casks, whisky barrels, boatbuilding and veneers.

Some examples of its uses are shown here.

ONLINE

Follow the link on the Digital Zone for a wood database.

BEECH

Cost: Quite expensive

Working properties: Beech is hard and very strong but is prone to warping. Despite it being heavy and difficult to work with hand tools, it machines and turns well. Beech also responds superbly to steam-bending and glues and finishes well. It is not suitable for outdoor work because it is not durable when exposed to changes in moisture. Beech is a very light pinkish brown colour and has a close even grain.

Typical uses: Children's toys, wooden spoons, chairs, workbenches, flooring, carpenter's mallets, veneers, plywood, and turned objects such as rolling pins.

Some examples of its uses are shown here.

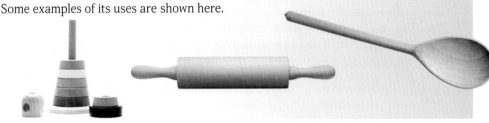

MAHOGANY

Cost: Expensive

Working properties: Mahogany is a reasonably durable, strong material that glues and finishes well. It is easy to work with using both hand and machine tools. The colour of mahogany can vary from pink to reddish brown.

Typical uses: Veneers, plywood, turned items such as banister spindles, quality indoor furniture, window frames, door frames and boat fittings, for example, interior trims and wall panels.

Some examples of its uses are shown here.

DON'T FORGET

Veneers (thin layers of wood) such as mahogany, are applied to a base material (often chipboard or plywood) to make maximum use of the expensive timber.

MERANTI (PHILIPPINE MAHOGANY)

Cost: Quite expensive

Working properties: Meranti is often seen as a substitute for the more expensive timber, Mahogany. It is not nearly as hard nor as strong, and lacks the durability and stability of a true mahogany. Due to its low density, it is typically easy to work with using both hand and machine tools. It glues, stains and finishes well. Meranti varies in colour from a light reddish brown to a deep reddish brown.

Typical uses: Plywood, veneers, interior furniture, lightweight structural framing, mouldings and trims, for example, skirting boards and window sills.

Some examples of its uses are shown here.

VIDEO LINK

Watch the video about the value of hardwoods on the Digital Zone.

ONLINE

Go online to download the worksheet on research of wood.

THINGS TO DO AND THINK ABOUT

1. Describe the appearance of Ash.

2. Which hardwood might you choose to make whisky barrels from?

3. Why is Beech mainly reserved for products with an interior use?

4. Meranti is often seen as a substitute for Mahogany. Describe three differences between the two materials.

5. List three typical uses for Ash, Oak, Beech, Mahogany and Meranti.

ONLINE TEST

Test yourself on hardwoods at www.brightredbooks.net

MANUFACTURED BOARDS

Manufactured boards are used extensively in the mass production of furniture, and in the construction industry. They are manmade and have been developed over time. The main advantage of manufactured boards over natural timbers is that are they are available in large sheet sizes – usually 2440 × 1220 mm. They are strong, flat and stable and are cheap to make.

In the exam for Practical Woodworking, you will be expected to identify, give accurate information in terms of their working properties, and suggest a specific use for a variety of commonly used manufactured boards. The five manufactured boards that you should know about are Plywood, Blockboard, Chipboard, Hardboard and MDF. The following provides all the information you need to know.

PLYWOOD

Cost: Fairly inexpensive

Composition: Plywood is made from thin sheets of wood (veneers) that are glued together with the grain direction of each layer at 90° to each other. To reduce warping, there is always an odd number of layers, for example, three, five or seven. The more layers used, the stronger the plywood becomes. Common thicknesses are 4, 6, 9, 12, 16, 19 and 25 mm.

Working properties: Plywood is a very strong material that is fairly resistant to shrinkage and warping. Although it is easy to work, shape and bend, it is prone to splitting when being cut or planed. You can, however, nail or screw close to the edge of plywood without it splitting. Different grades of plywood are available; marine grade should be used if the product is to be used outside or in damp conditions.

Typical uses: Interior wall lining, door fronts, furniture-making, cabinet backs, drawer bottoms. Marine grade plywood is often used in boatbuilding.

An example of its uses is shown here.

BLOCKBOARD

Cost: Expensive

Composition: Blockboard is a wood-based panel that is made by gluing strips of 25 mm softwood, edge to edge, which is then sandwiched between veneers of a decorative softwood or hardwood. For added strength, the grains of the veneers are attached at 90° to the core strips. A commonly used thickness is 18 mm.

Fire door keep shut

Working properties: Blockboard is a very strong, rigid material that is rather heavy and does not warp easily. Due to the type of glue used in its manufacture, it is normally intended for interior use only.

Typical uses: High quality furniture, table tops, shelves, partition walls and fire doors.

An example of its uses is shown here.

CHIPBOARD

Cost: Inexpensive

Composition: Chipboard is made from waste wood particles, such as wood chips, sawmill shavings and sawdust, which are mixed with glue and compressed into a sheet. The strength, appearance and durability of chipboard can be enhanced by applying a plastic laminate coating or a hardwood veneer.

Common thicknesses are 12, 16, 19 and 25 mm.

contd

Working properties: Chipboard is heavy, with a hard, smooth surface and a softer core. Because it is quite brittle, it is prone to breaking up when screws are driven in close to the edges. If it becomes wet, it breaks up easily, and is therefore not suitable for exterior use. Chipboard is not as strong as plywood or blockboard.

Typical uses: Shelving, loft flooring, wall partitions and (when veneered) kitchen worktops, kitchen cupboards, and flat-pack furniture such as wardrobes.

An example of its uses is shown here.

HARDBOARD

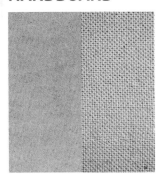

Cost: Inexpensive

Composition: Hardboard is made by mixing very fine sawmill shavings, sawdust and glue into a woodpulp which is then compressed into a sheet. It is mainly only available in thin sheet thicknesses of 3 and 6mm.

Working properties: Hardboard is lightweight and is easy to cut, shape and bend. It is not very strong and is rather like a strong cardboard. Untreated hardboard absorbs water readily and is therefore not suitable for exterior use. One side of hardboard is smooth and the other is rough.

ONLINE

For videos and worksheets on this topic, head to www.brightredbooks.net

Typical uses: Lightweight interior door panels, clipboards, backs of wardrobes and cabinets, cheap drawer bottoms, templates, flooring underlay, lightweight stage scenery and signs.

An example of its use is shown here.

MDF (MEDIUM DENSITY FIBREBOARD)

Cost: Fairly inexpensive

Composition: MDF is also made by mixing very fine sawmill shavings, sawdust and glue into a woodpulp which is then compressed into a sheet. Common thicknesses are 3, 6, 9, 12, 19 and 25mm.

DON'T FORGET

Hardboard is not as strong as plywood but is quite a bit cheaper. This makes it useful for some larger projects.

Working properties: MDF is a very heavy, strong and stable sheet material. It has an excellent flat, smooth surface finish which can be veneered, covered in a plastic laminate or painted. MDF is very easy to shape into curves and work with using both hand and machine tools. MDF is better suited to interior use.

Typical uses: Skirting boards, mouldings, pattern-making, doors, wall partitions, shelving, kitchen cupboards, snooker tables, and flat-pack furniture such as wardrobes.

An example of its uses is shown here.

 THINGS TO DO AND THINK ABOUT

1. State the standard manufactured board sheet size used in the UK.
2. List three advantages of using manufactured board over natural timber.
3. Explain how plywood is made.
4. What does MDF stand for?
5. Which manufactured board might you choose to make fire doors from?
6. List three typical uses for Plywood, Blockboard, Chipboard, Hardboard and MDF.

VIDEO LINK

Watch the video about how to construct an MDF door on the Digital Zone.

ONLINE TEST

Test yourself on manufactured boards at www.brightredbooks.net

HAMMERS AND NAILS

CROSS PEIN HAMMER

A cross pein hammer is designed for light nailing work. The cross pein end is used to start a panel pin between your finger and thumb before the rest of the pin is driven in using the striking face.

The cross pein hammer has a wooden shaft, made from either ash or hickory, which is fitted into the metal head of the hammer. To prevent the head flying off during use, the shaft is secured in place by a metal or wooden wedge.

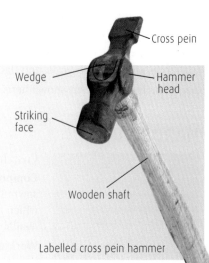

Cross pein

Wedge

Hammer head

Striking face

Wooden shaft

Labelled cross pein hammer

VIDEO LINK

Watch the clip on how to choose and use a hammer at www.brightredbooks.net

CLAW HAMMER

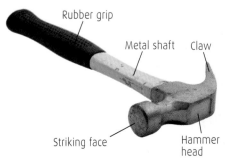

Rubber grip

Metal shaft

Claw

Striking face

Hammer head

Labelled metal-handled claw hammer

The claw hammer being used to remove a nail from a piece of wood

DON'T FORGET

You should hold the end of the shaft and swing the hammer from the elbow to drive the nail into the wood.

A claw hammer is designed for heavy nailing work and removing nails, and it is available with either a wooden shaft, made from either ash or hickory, or an alloy metal shaft with a rubber grip. Just as with the cross pein hammer, to prevent the head flying off during use, the shaft is secured in place by a metal or wooden wedge.

PINCERS

Pincers tend to be used to remove thin nails, nails that claw hammers cannot grip, or nails that have been accidently bent during hammering.

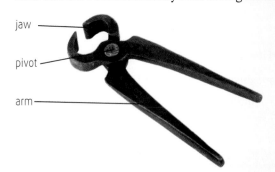

jaw

pivot

arm

VIDEO LINK

For an overview of hammers, check out the video at www.brightredbooks.net

The pincers in use

To remove a bent nail, the nail is gripped between the jaws of the pincers then the pincers are rolled back towards you. To prevent damaging the wood underneath, scrap wood should be placed under the jaw of the pincer.

NAIL PUNCH

A nail punch is used to drive the head of a nail or panel pin below the surface of the wood.

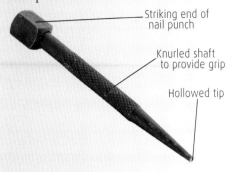

Striking end of nail punch

Knurled shaft to provide grip

Hollowed tip

The nail punch in use

The hollowed tip of the nail punch fits over the head of a nail then the head of the nail punch is struck with a hammer.

NAILS

Round Head Nail

A round head nail is mainly used for general construction work, particularly in the building industry. The head of a round head nail cannot be punched below the surface of the wood. Round head nails range in length from 18–150 mm.

Oval Brad Nail

An oval brad nail is used for joinery and flooring. The shape of the shaft of the oval brad helps prevent the wood from splitting when it is driven into the wood. The head of the oval brad can be hidden below the surface of the wood using a nail punch. Oval brads range in length from 12–65 mm.

Panel Pins

A panel pin is a small thin nail that is mainly used for fixing thin sheet material to the bottom of boxes or the backs of cabinets. Panel pins are normally used along with glue to hold a joint together while the glue is setting. To improve the finish of the piece of work, the head of the panel pin can easily be punched below the surface of the wood with a nail punch. Panel pins range in length from 8–40 mm.

 THINGS TO DO AND THINK ABOUT

1. Sketch and label a cross pein hammer.
2. Sketch and label a claw hammer.
3. Describe the different uses of a cross pein hammer and a claw hammer.
4. State which woods hammer shafts are made from.
5. Sketch and label a nail punch and explain why the shaft section has been knurled.
6. State which nail you would use to nail down a floorboard.
7. Describe the differences between the round head nail, the oval brad nail and panel pins.

SCREWS AND SCREWDRIVERS

Countersink Head   Round head

Shank

Thread

Tip

Countersink screw   Round head screw

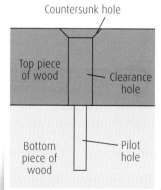

Countersink rose

Countersunk hole

Top piece of wood   Clearance hole

Bottom piece of wood   Pilot hole

SCREWS

Screws are an effective way of joining two or more pieces of wood together on either a temporary or permanent basis – they are only joined permanently when glue is applied. Screws are stronger, neater and more accurate than nails and can be easily withdrawn, meaning the parts can be separated without damage.

The two most common types are **Countersink** and **Round head** screws which are shown below. You will notice that the two wood screws are the same basic shape, with the main difference being the shape of the head of the screw.

SCREW HEADS

Countersink Screw

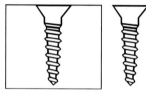

Countersink screw head level with the surface of the wood

Round head Screw

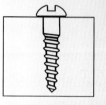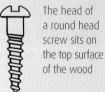

The head of a round head screw sits on the top surface of the wood

The countersink screw is the most commonly used general purpose screw in the workshop. A countersink rose creates a chamfer in the entrance to a drilled hole, allowing a countersink screw head to go level or slightly below the surface of the material. As a result, countersink heads are commonly used in situations where the screw must be partially or fully concealed or where a flat surface must be maintained.

The round head screw is also known as the domed head screw. The round head sits on the surface of the material unlike the countersink head (as shown). A common use for a round head screw is for attaching fittings to wood, for example, a tee hinge on a shed door or a latch on a garden gate. Round head screws can look quite decorative, especially if they are made from brass.

Procedure for driving in a Wood Screw

When driving a screw into a piece of wood, care should be taken not to split the wood. The following procedure is recommended when joining two pieces of wood. This makes it easier to drive in the screw and prevents the wood from splitting.

Stage one
A **clearance hole**, which is larger than the thread of the screw, is drilled into the top piece of wood.

Stage two
Next, a **pilot hole**, which is smaller than the diameter of the thread of the screw, should then be drilled into the bottom piece of wood.

Stage three
If the screw is required to lie flat with the surface of the wood, the top of the clearance hole should be countersunk using a countersink rose.

DON'T FORGET

When selecting the length of screw required for the job, you should always consider the thicknesses of the two pieces of wood, so that the screw does not penetrate through the underside.

DRIVE AND SCREWDRIVER TYPES

If you look closely at the head of a screw, be it a round head or a countersink, you will see it has a straight slot or a cross shape. This is known as the type of **drive**. The end of a screwdriver is made to fit the type of drive. Screwdrivers come in many shapes and sizes depending on their intended use, in terms of length of screw and type of drive. The two main types of screwdrivers we are going to look at in this chapter are the **straight head** and **cross head**.

contd

Straight Head Screwdriver

A straight head screwdriver, shown below, is designed to fit into the head of a screw which has a slotted drive. When using a straight head screwdriver, care should be taken not to apply too much pressure which could cause the tip of the screwdriver to slip out of the slotted head and cause damage to the surface of the work piece.

Slotted Drive

Handle

Blade

Tip

Parts of a screwdriver

A slotted drive, shown above, has a single straight recess across the screw head

A decorative brass countersink screw with a slotted drive

A black japanned (intended for exterior use) round head screw with a slotted drive

Cross Head Screwdriver

There are two types of cross head screwdriver, a Phillips and a Pozidriv (as shown below), with the Pozidriv version being the more commonly used. The cross head screwdriver is less likely than the straight head screwdriver to slip out and cause damage to the surface of the workpiece.

Enlarged view of the tip of a Phillips cross head screwdriver

Enlarged view of the tip of a Pozidriv cross head screwdriver

ONLINE

For more information on screws check out the link at www.brightredbooks.net

Phillips and Pozidriv drive

As you can see from the picture below, the drive of a Phillips and Pozidriv both have a cross shape cut into the centre.

Philips drive from above

A screw with a Philips drive

Pozidriv drive from above

Countersink screw with a Pozidriv drive

THINGS TO DO AND THINK ABOUT

1. State the name and sketch a screw you would use if you required the head of the screw to lie level with the surface of the material.
2. Suggest what might happen if you tried to drive a screw into a piece of wood without having drilled a pilot hole first.
3. State the name and sketch the head of a screw which a straight head screwdriver is designed to fit into.
4. Describe the recommended procedure for screwing two pieces of wood together that makes it easier to drive in the screw and prevents the wood from splitting.

ONLINE TEST

Test yourself on screwdrivers and screws at www.brightredbooks.net

WORK BENCH AND HAND DRILLS

WORK BENCH AND BENCH VICE

One of the most important pieces of equipment in any workshop is the work bench and bench vice. Whether you are cutting, drilling, chiselling or even sanding a piece of wood, it is often easier and indeed safer to secure the workpiece in the bench vice.

The bench vice is mounted on to the underside of the bench so that the jaws are level with the top. The metal jaws tend to be covered with wooden jaw pads to prevent them from damaging any fragile material while it's being held in place.
The jaw pads, also known as vice

Bench vice

Work bench

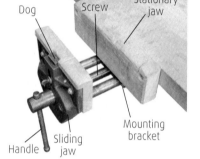

Dog Screw Stationary jaw

Handle Sliding jaw Mounting bracket

Main parts of a bench vice

cheeks, are usually made from a hardwood such as beech, and are screwed into the jaws with a countersink screw so that the screw is flat with the surface of the cheek, and the screw head will not make an indent on the workpiece being held in the vice. The wooden cheeks can of course be unscrewed and replaced if they become worn or damaged. The handle is turned clockwise or anticlockwise to either open or close the jaws.

BENCH HOOK/SAWING BOARD

Top stock

Bottom stock

Main parts of a bench hook

A bench hook, also known as a sawing board, is mainly used when sawing wood across the grain. By using a bench hook, you will prevent your work bench from being damaged when the saw breaks through the wood.

A bench hook held securely in place in a bench vice. The work piece is held against the top stock, while the bottom stock is held in the bench vice

HAND TOOLS

Bradawl

A bradawl is a hand tool used to make pilot holes in wood for small screws or large nails, and for marking centres in wood to guide a drill. To create a pilot hole with a bradawl, the small metal tip is held across the grain then the handle is twisted into the wood.

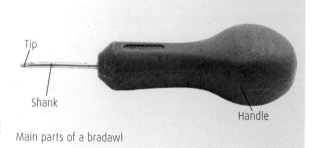

Tip

Shank

Handle

Main parts of a bradawl

The bradawl creating a pilot hole in a piece of wood

contd

Hand Drill

The hand drill is used to accurately drill small holes in wood. It's quick and easy to operate and can accommodate drill bits with a shank of up to 10 mm. It is a useful tool for quickly drilling a pilot hole in wood using a twist drill, or a countersunk hole using a countersink rose. The hand drill comes in handy when you need to drill a hole in a confined space.

Main parts of a hand drill

Jaws · Chuck · Turning handle · Main handle

Hand drill in use

Drilling a hole using a Hand Drill

When drilling with a hand drill, you should make sure your workpiece is being held firmly in place. If drilling all the way through, your workpiece should be clamped down with waste wood placed underneath. With the position for the hole clearly marked with a cross, place the tip of the drill bit in position, making sure the drill bit is at 90° to the surface of the workpiece, then steadily turn the handle clockwise while applying a gentle pressure. Once you have completed your drill hole, if you continue to turn the handle as you pull the drill bit out of the hole, you will find that it is not only easier to remove the drill bit, but you'll also achieve a cleaner finish to the hole.

ONLINE

Learn more about drills by following the link at www.brightredbooks.net

Hand (Carpenter's) Brace

The hand brace is a powerful drilling tool that is used to accurately drill large holes in wood. The sweep of a hand brace describes the space required to make one complete turn of the sweep handle. The common sweep size is 250 mm. The ratchet allows the brace to be used in a confined space when a full turn is not possible.

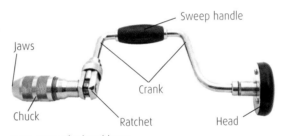

Main parts of a hand brace

Sweep handle · Jaws · Crank · Chuck · Ratchet · Head

The hand brace can be used either vertically or horizontally. When using it horizontally, you can place the head of the brace against your chest so that you can use your body weight to apply more pressure to the drill bit if necessary. When drilling a hole with a hand brace you should follow the same steps as you would for the hand drill; however, it is even more important that care should be taken to ensure that the bit makes its exit into waste wood. A recognised technique for preventing ragged holes when drilling all the way through a piece of wood with a hand brace is to work halfway through the wood from each side. As soon as the point of the bit shows through, turn the wood and drill from the other side.

Hand brace in use

Point of the bit beginning to show through

DON'T FORGET

Hand drills and braces can be used anywhere, including remote locations without a power supply – even a cordless drill needs a power supply to charge the battery once it goes flat.

THINGS TO DO AND THINK ABOUT

1. State a reason for fitting wooden cheeks to the metal jaws of a bench vice.
2. Suggest why the wooden cheeks are often fitted to the jaws of the vice using countersink screws.
3. State why a sawing board is used when sawing a piece of wood.
4. State the main use of a hand drill.
5. State the main use of a hand brace.
6. Describe how you prevent wood from splitting when a hole is drilled all the way through it using a hand brace.

ONLINE TEST

Test yourself on the work bench and hand drills at www.brightredbooks.net

CUTTING

Cutting wood to length, shape or size is something you'll have to do frequently during Practical Woodworking. With different tooth sizes, there is a handsaw for every type of work. The cut/finish will differ depending on the tooth size.

SAW TERMINOLOGY

Heel: The end closest to the handle.

Toe: The end farthest from the handle.

Front: The edge with the teeth (the bottom edge).

Back: Opposite the front (the top edge).

Teeth: Small sharp points along the cutting edge of the saw.

Rake: The angle of the front face of the tooth relative to a line perpendicular to the length of the saw. Teeth designed to cut across the grain (Crosscutting) are generally not as steep as teeth designed to cut with the grain (known as Ripping).

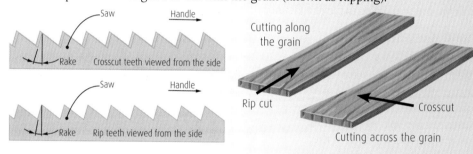

Teeth Per Inch (TPI)

A common measurement of the number of teeth residing in any one inch (25mm) length of the saw blade. As a rule, a saw with a higher number of TPI gives a finer finish than larger toothed handsaws with a much smaller number of TPI.

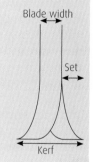

Kerf

Width of the saw cut. On most saws, the kerf is wider than the saw blade because the teeth are flared out sideways (the "set"). This allows the blade to move through the cut easily without getting stuck (binding).

SAW TYPES

Tenon Saw

Handle

Steel or brass back

Saw blade

contd

The **Tenon saw** is traditionally a general purpose saw used to make straight cuts in wood such as tenons or other work of similar size. The solid steel or brass back fitted to the saw blade helps keep the blade in tension and provides sufficient weight to feed the saw through the wood. Standard tenon saws have a 15 TPI blade and are available in lengths of 250–300 mm.

When cutting with a tenon saw you place a **bench hook/sawing board** into a **bench vice**, secure it in place by tightening the vice, then hold your workpiece firmly against the bench hook.

Coping Saw

Coping saws are designed for cutting curves, shapes and slots in wood. In the event that you need to cut a larger sheet and the frame begins to get in the way, the thin blade can be rotated to cut at any angle by adjusting the end pins. Standard coping saws have either a 14 TPI or a 24 TPI blade which are 165 mm in length. The teeth of a coping saw blade point backwards towards the handle, cutting on the back stroke rather than the forward stroke.

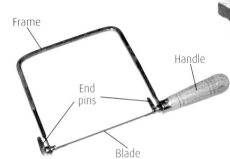

Frame

Handle

End pins

Blade

Bench hook/sawing board

Rip Saw

A rip saw is used to make a cut parallel to the direction of the grain of the workpiece. When you cut along the grain, this is known as ripping. Standard rip saws have a 4½ TPI blade and are available in lengths of 500–650 mm.

Crosscut Saw

A **crosscut saw** is used to make a cut at a right angle to the direction of the grain of the workpiece. When you cut across the grain this is known as a crosscut. Standard crosscut saws have a 8 TPI blade and are available in lengths of 500–650 mm. This is a good general purpose tooth size.

Panel Saw

The **panel saw** has a 10 TPI blade and is a finer-toothed crosscut saw. It is for cutting across the grain and gives a finer finish than larger toothed crosscut saws. It is also used for cutting manmade boards such as plywood.

 THINGS TO DO AND THINK ABOUT

1. What is the meaning of the term TPI?
2. Draw and label the main parts of a tenon saw and coping saw and explain the main differences between the two saws and their uses.
3. Describe the main difference between a rip saw and a crosscut saw and their uses.

 DON'T FORGET

Using a bench hook will prevent your work bench from being damaged by the continual cutting.

DON'T FORGET

It is important that you hold your work securely while carrying out a saw cut.

VIDEO LINK

Watch the clip on ripping short stock at www.brightredbooks.net

VIDEO LINK

For more on saws and sawing, watch the video on the Digital Zone.

 ONLINE TEST

Test your knowledge of saws at www.brightredbooks.net

CHISELS 1

A carpenter chopping out a joint using a mortise chisel and mallet

CHISELLING

Wood chisels have two main uses, **paring** and **chopping** wood. Paring refers to the removal of small shavings using only hand pressure, and chopping refers to removing large areas of waste wood by driving the chisel with blows from a mallet. Paring is often used where intricate woodworking is needed, such as finishing a joint to achieve a tight fit; chopping is mainly used when creating joints.

Paring down a cross-halving joint with a bevel edge chisel. The chisel is pushed forward by one hand and supported by the other

Mallet

Handle

Head

A mallet is used to tap or strike the handle of a wood chisel.

PARTS OF A CHISEL

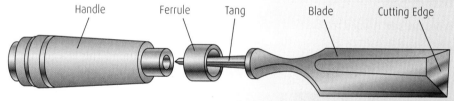

Handle   Ferrule   Tang   Blade   Cutting Edge

Parts of a chisel

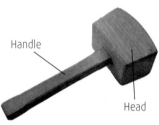

The stainless-steel ferrule is fitted tightly round the neck of the handle

Handle: The handle tends to be round in shape and is made of wood or plastic.

Ferrule: The ferrule is a brass or stainless-steel ring which is fitted to the handle to protect it from splitting when the tang is fitted into it, or when it is struck by a mallet.

Tang: The tang is the part of the blade that fits into the handle to fix them both together. It is usually square in shape which tapers to a point.

Blade: The blade of a chisel comes in a variety of shapes depending on its use and is made from a strong, tool steel.

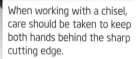

DON'T FORGET

When working with a chisel, care should be taken to keep both hands behind the sharp cutting edge.

Cutting edge: The cutting edge is found on the end of the blade and is honed to a razor-sharp edge.

The measurement of a wood chisel refers to the width of the blade's cutting edge. The width of a chisel commonly ranges from 3–50mm, typically rising in 2mm increments.

A range of widths of chisels are available

TYPES OF CHISEL

Bevel Edge Chisel

The bevel edge chisel is a good general purpose chisel. It has a thin blade which is bevelled along its length on both sides. Its thin, sharp blade can be used for gently paring away a slice of wood, or to shave small amounts away by using the chisel by hand. The bevel edge chisel is not designed to withstand the force of heavy mallet blows.

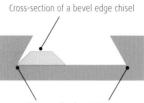

Cross-section of a bevel edge chisel

Corners of a dovetail joint

Due to its thin and bevelled blade, it is suited to cutting into angled corners, such as in dovetails

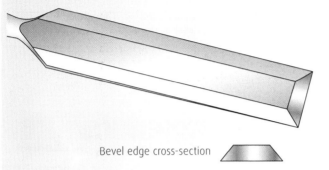

Bevel edge cross-section

Blade of a bevel edge chisel

Firmer Chisel

The firmer chisel is a good general purpose chisel that is mainly suited to the heavier work of cutting out deeper joints. It has a thick, flat, rectangular blade with square edges (without a bevel). As the name suggests, its thick, sturdier blade will remove waste wood from joints either by using the chisel by hand, or with medium-to-heavy mallet blows.

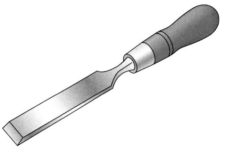

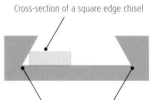

Cross-section of a square edge chisel

Corners of a dovetail joint

Although not suitable for cutting out the corners of a dovetail, the firmer chisel is ideal for creating joints where you need to maintain sharp, 90° corners

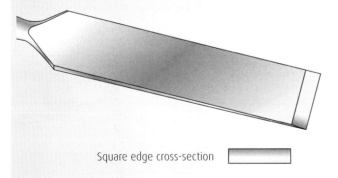

Square edge cross-section

Blade of a firmer chisel

 ONLINE

For more about chisels, follow the link at www.brightredbooks.net

 THINGS TO DO AND THINK ABOUT

1. Describe the difference between paring and chopping with a chisel.

2. State the reason why a ferrule is fitted to a chisel handle.

3. State the purpose of the tang.

4. Make a labelled sketch of a bevel edge chisel and a firmer chisel.

 ONLINE TEST

Test yourself on chisels at www.brightredbooks.net

CHISELS 2

TYPES OF CHISEL

Mortise Chisel

Mortise chisels are used with a mallet to chop out mortises. A mortise is the rectangular slot found in a mortise and tenon joint. Due to this heavy duty work, its blade needs to be able to withstand the continuous heavy mallet blows and leverage applied when removing the waste wood. The mortise chisel has a much thicker and stronger blade than those of the other chisels. The other differences can be seen below. A mortise chisel has two ferrules fitted to prevent the handle from splitting from the repeated mallet blows, and it also has a leather washer fitted between the blade and the handle to act as a shock absorber. Mortise chisels are usually available in blade widths of 6, 8, 9 and 13mm.

Cutting edge   Blade   Ferrule   Handle   Ferrule

Parts of a mortise chisel

A piece of tape or a pen mark can be applied to the chisel to mark the required depth of cut, or a steel rule can be used to measure the depth of the mortise after each series of cuts.

Tape wrapped around a mortise chisel to ensure the mortise is cut to the correct depth

DON'T FORGET

When striking a chisel with a mallet, the workpiece should be held firmly in a vice or clamped to the work bench.

VIDEO LINK

Check out the clip on how to cut a mortise and tenon joint at www.brightredbooks.net

VIDEO LINK

Learn how to use a honing guide at www.brightredbooks.net

SHARPENING A CHISEL

Chisels need frequent sharpening. The sharpening process is also known as honing. A blunt chisel is not only more dangerous to use than a sharp chisel but is also more difficult to use. This may seem contradictory, but sharp chisels require less force to be applied and give you greater control. The cutting edge of a chisel has two angles, a ground angle and a sharpening angle. The ground angle is created using a grinding wheel and the sharpening angle is achieved using an oilstone and a honing guide.

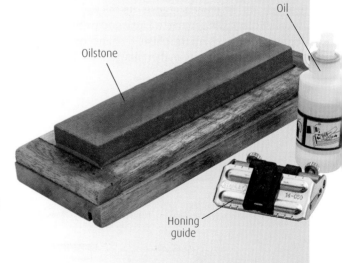

Oil

Oilstone

Honing guide

Oil can

Oil for lubrication

Bevel edge chisel blade

Oilstone

Honing guide

contd

A bevel edge chisel blade is initially ground on a grinding wheel to an angle of 25° before the tip of the blade has a cutting angle honed to 30°. With experience, you may be able to create a honed tip to 30° by hand; however, it is far easier to guarantee that you maintain the correct angle by using a honing guide. The chisel blade is fitted into the honing guide, clamped in place, then gently moved backwards and forwards on the oilstone to achieve a constant, accurate angle.

The blade is gently moved backwards and forwards on the oilstone

After the sharpening angle has been honed, you will notice a fine **burr** has been produced on the underside of the blade. To remove this, the blade should be placed flat on the oilstone, then moved gently left to right. It is important that the blade is kept completely flat at this stage. The blade should then be wiped clean of any oil before use.

Bevel edge, firmer and mortise chisels are all ground to slightly different angles (as shown below).

To remove the burr, the blade should be placed flat on the oilstone, then moved gently left to right

The Burr

There it is!

This side was just sharpened

After the sharpening angle has been honed, you will notice a fine **burr** has been produced on the underside of the blade

A bevel edge chisel has a cutting edge with a ground angle between 20° and 30°. The finer angle means that the blade is very sharp but may blunt more easily.

A firmer chisel has a cutting edge with a ground angle between 25° and 35°, giving the cutting edge greater strength when heavy mallet blows are needed.

A mortise chisel has a cutting edge with a ground angle between 30° and 40°, giving the mortise chisel a sharp edge that can withstand heavy duty work.

BEVEL

20°–30°

FIRMER

25°–35°

MORTISE

30°–40°

VIDEO LINK

View the clip at www.brightredbooks.net on how to sharpen a chisel.

THINGS TO DO AND THINK ABOUT

1. State the purpose of the leather washer found on a mortise chisel.

2. Make a labelled sketch of a mortise chisel.

3. State why the blade of a mortise chisel is thicker and stronger than those of the other chisels.

4. State what the process of sharpening a chisel is known as.

5. Bevel edge, firmer and mortise chisels are all ground to slightly different angles. State the suggested ground angle for each chisel.

ONLINE TEST

Test yourself on chisels at www.brightredbooks.net

PLANES

PLANES AND PLANING

Planes have two main uses, planing wood down to a specific size and smoothing the surface of a piece of wood. The two most commonly used hand planes in a school workshop are the **jack plane** and the **smoothing plane**. The two planes are similar in appearance; only their lengths are different.

Jack Plane

The jack plane is a general purpose plane which is mainly used to plane wood flat and down to size. The jack plane is often used initially to remove any marks left on the wood by the saw. The length of the body ranges from 350–400 mm and the blade is usually between 50–60 mm in width. It is the long length of its body that helps to create a flat surface, particularly on long lengths of wood.

A jack plane

Smoothing Plane

The smoothing plane is much shorter than the jack plane with the length of its body ranging from 230–250 mm in length with a blade width of 50 mm. The lighter, shorter smoothing plane, as its name suggests, is used to smooth the surface of wood prior to applying a finish. It removes thin shavings of wood to leave a clean, smooth finish which is often superior to that left by sandpaper.

A smoothing plane

Main parts of a Plane

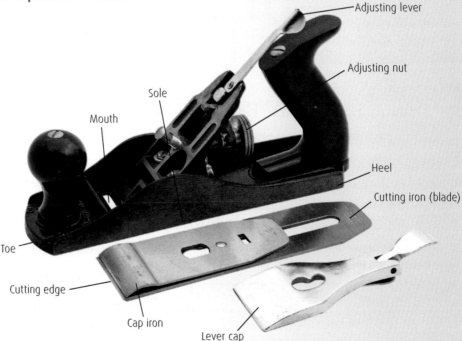

The main parts and methods of adjustment are common to both planes

contd

DON'T FORGET

The shorter smoothing plane is for fine finishing, while the longer jack plane is more suited to removing excess wood and producing a smooth edge on longer pieces of wood.

VIDEO LINK

Check out the clip about the anatomy of a plane at www.brightredbooks.net

Setting a Plane

In order to achieve a smooth, clean cut, a plane must have a sharp blade and be adjusted correctly. Although a plane is made up of a lot of different parts, the four main parts of the jack and smoothing plane that you should be familiar with are the **cap iron**, **cutting iron** (also known as the blade), **adjusting lever** and **adjusting nut**.

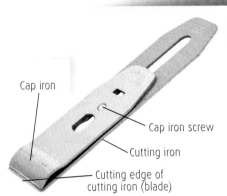

Cap iron

Cap iron screw

Cutting iron

Cutting edge of cutting iron (blade)

The assembled cap iron and cutting iron

The cap iron and the cutting iron are held together with a screw. They are removable from the body of the plane for sharpening and maintenance. The cap iron clears out the shavings and prevents the mouth of the plane from getting choked. It is important that the cap iron is set a suitable distance back from the cutting edge of the cutting iron. When working with softwoods or removing a lot of waste wood from a workpiece, you should set the cap iron around 2 mm away from the cutting edge. This gap should be reduced to around 0.5 mm when you are working with hardwood, or when you wish to leave a very clean, smooth finish on your wood, prior to applying a finish.

ADJUSTING THE PLANE

Once the cap iron and the cutting iron (blade) have been fixed in place, the final setting and fine tuning of the blade can be done. Firstly, turn the plane upside down and look along the sole to see if the blade is protruding. Turn the adjusting nut until no more than 0.5 mm of the blade is showing above the sole. Now use the adjusting lever to get the cutting edge parallel to the sole. A few trial cuts can be made on a scrap piece of wood so that you can use the adjusting nut to get the depth of cut you need.

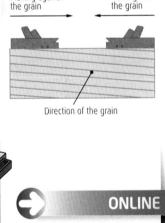

Adjusting lever

Adjusting nut

The adjusting lever and adjusting nut

PLANING TIPS

When planing a piece of wood along the edge, it is important to plane with the grain. Planing against the grain will result in a very rough, broken surface.

Planing end grain can often be difficult and care must be taken to prevent splitting the wood. To prevent this, it will be necessary to plane the wood from both ends working towards the centre or to cramp a piece of scrap wood against the furthest edge of the workpiece (as shown).

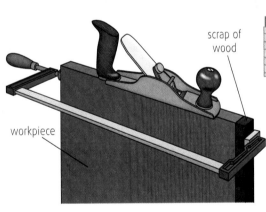

scrap of wood

workpiece

Planing against the grain

Planing with the grain

Direction of the grain

ONLINE

Learn more about planes by following the link at www.brightredbooks.net

THINGS TO DO AND THINK ABOUT

1. Describe two uses for a plane.
2. State the two most commonly used planes in a school workshop and describe the difference between them.
3. State the purpose of the cap iron.
4. State what the cutting iron is also known as.
5. State how far the cap iron should be set back from the cutting edge of the cutting iron when you are removing a lot of waste wood from a workpiece.
6. Describe how you would check if the blade of the plane was parallel to the sole and what you could do if it was protruding too much to one side.
7. State what part of the plane you would adjust if the blade was cutting too deep and digging into the wood.
8. Describe a technique that could be used to prevent splitting your workpiece when planing end grain.

ONLINE TEST

Test yourself on planes at www.brightredbooks.net

SPECIALIST PLANES 1

PLOUGH PLANE

The plough plane is used to cut a groove parallel to an edge.

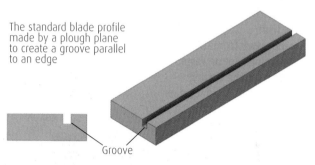

The standard blade profile made by a plough plane to create a groove parallel to an edge

Groove

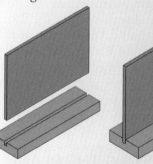

A groove is cut into a workpiece to receive materials such as plywood or hardboard for cabinet backs and drawer bases

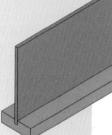

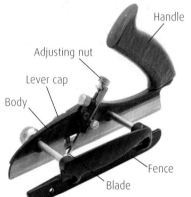

Handle

Adjusting nut

Lever cap

Body

Fence

Blade

Main parts of a plough plane

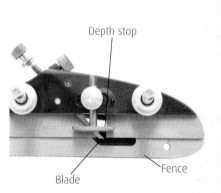

Depth stop

Blade

Fence

Depth stop and adjustable fence of a plough plane

The plough plane has a depth stop to determine the depth of cut made by the blade and an adjustable fence which controls the distance the groove is from the edge of the wood. The adjusting nut offers precise control of the thickness of shavings made by the blade.

Setting the depth stop: set the required depth of cut by adjusting the distance from the depth stop to the tip of the blade.

Setting the fence: adjusting the distance of the fence to the edge of the blade controls the distance of the groove to the edge of the wood.

The plough plane has many interchangeable blades of various widths ranging from 3–12.5 mm.

Cutting a Groove

A typical blade of a plough plane

When cutting a groove in your workpiece, start cutting the groove at the front and work your way to the back of the wood while keeping the fence tight against the edge.

REBATE PLANE

VIDEO LINK

Watch the anatomy of a rebate plane video at www.brightredbooks.net

The rebate plane is used to cut rebates along the edge or across the end of a piece of wood.

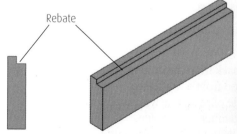

Rebate

The rebate blade profile made by a rebate plane

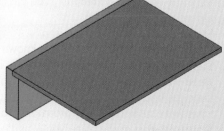

A rebate is cut into a workpiece to receive materials such as plywood or hardboard for cabinet backs and box bases

contd

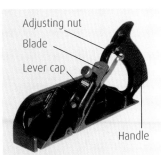

Main parts of a rebate plane

A typical blade for a rebate plane can cut rebates up to 38mm wide

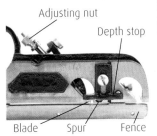

Like the plough plane, the rebate plane has an adjustable depth of cut, fence and depth stop

Setting the depth stop: set the required depth of cut by adjusting the distance from the depth stop to the tip of the blade.

Setting the fence: set the required width of rebate by adjusting the distance from the fence to the edge of the blade.

Cutting a Rebate

To ensure a clean cut is made when cutting a rebate across the grain of a piece of wood, it is recommended to rotate the spur into the cutting position to allow it to cut the fibres of the wood ahead of the blade.

Start cutting at the front of the wood and begin to work back towards the end closest to you, keeping the fence tight against the edge and the plane upright

You will know when the rebate plane has cut down to the required depth when the depth stop makes contact with the workpiece and the plane stops cutting wood

COMBINATION PLANE

As the name suggests, the more sophisticated combination plane combines the functions of a variety of specialist planes in one tool. The method of cutting and the available adjustments are the same as that of both the plough and rebate planes.

The combination plane is supplied with various blades which make it capable of creating the variety of decorative profiles shown below.

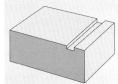

Standard blade profile

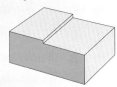

Rebate blade profile

Beading blade profile

Tongue cutting blade profile

A beading blade is an example of a typical blade used in the combination plane

THINGS TO DO AND THINK ABOUT

1. State what a plough plane is used for.
2. Sketch the profile made by a standard plough plane blade.
3. State the purpose of the fence on a plough plane.
4. State what a rebate plane is used for.
5. Sketch the profile made by a standard rebate plane blade.
6. Describe how you would set the depth stop to 8mm on a rebate plane.
7. Describe how you would set a rebate plane to cut a rebate of 5mm in width.
8. State the purpose of the spur on a rebate plane.

SPECIALIST PLANES 2

BLOCK PLANE

The block plane is intended to be used one-handed for small, fine, light work. It is particularly suitable for trimming end grain, mitres and running chamfers.

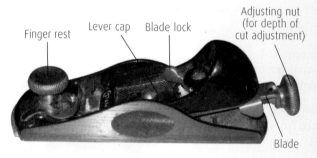

Finger rest   Lever cap   Blade lock   Adjusting nut (for depth of cut adjustment)

Blade

Main parts of a block plane

A block plane being used to run a chamfer along the edge of a piece of wood

BULL NOSE PLANE

The bull nose plane is another plane that is intended to be used one-handed for fine, intricate work. It is particularly suitable for trimming end grain, the shoulders of tenons and finishing rebates. It's a small plane at only 75–100 mm long with a narrow blade that is the full width of its body. With the blade sitting so close to the toe of the plane and the nose being removable, it can cut right into a tight corner.

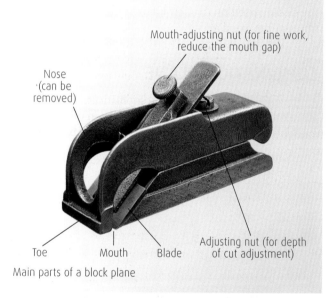

Mouth-adjusting nut (for fine work, reduce the mouth gap)

Nose (can be removed)

Toe   Mouth   Blade

Adjusting nut (for depth of cut adjustment)

Main parts of a block plane

HAND ROUTER

The hand router is used to level off the bottom of through and stopped housings. The bulk of the waste wood of the housing is initially cut out using a saw and chisel, then the hand router cutter is placed into the groove and pushed along the wood to make sure that the groove is cut down to a precise depth and is consistently flat across the joint.

A hand router being used to level off the bottom of a through housing joint

The depth stop is set to prevent the cutter from cutting below the required depth. To alter the depth of the cut, the cutter clamp is loosened then the cutter is either raised or lowered using the adjusting nut.

A typical cutter used in a hand router

SPOKE SHAVE

Although a spoke shave was originally designed to shape the spokes for the wheels of horse-drawn carts – hence the name – they are now mainly used to shape all kind of curves on workpieces. There are two types of spoke shave, a flat-bottomed and a round-bottomed. The flat-bottomed spoke shave is used to smooth an outside (convex) curve, whereas the round-bottomed spoke shave is used to smooth an inside (concave) curve. If a clean, smooth finish is to be obtained on the curves, care should be taken to always cut with the grain and never against it.

A convex curve   A concave curve

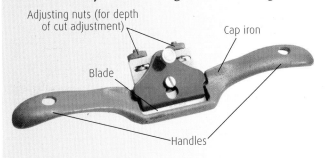

Adjusting nuts (for depth of cut adjustment)

Cap iron

Blade

Handles

Main parts of a spoke shave

A concave curve created using a spoke shave

SHARPENING EQUIPMENT

All plane, chisel and spoke shave blades must be kept sharp, otherwise they will not work efficiently. Sharpening a blade requires skill and needs lots of practice. It's a requirement of the N5 Practical Woodworking course that you are familiar with how a blade is sharpened. Sharpening a blade is done on an oilstone which is covered with a fine film of oil as a lubricant.

A plane is initially ground on a grinding wheel to an angle of 25° before the tip of the blade has a cutting angle honed to 30°. With experience, you may be able to create a honed tip to 30° by hand; however, it is far easier to guarantee that you maintain the correct angle by using a honing guide. The plane iron is fitted in to the honing guide, clamped in place, then gently moved backwards and forwards on the oilstone to achieve a constant, accurate angle.

After the sharpening angle has been honed, you will notice a fine burr has been produced on the underside of the blade. To remove this, the blade should be placed flat on the oilstone, then moved gently left to right. It is important that the blade is kept completely flat at this stage. The blade should then be wiped clean of any oil before use.

Oilstone   Oil

Honing guide

Sharpening equipment

Ground at 25°

Honed at 30°

The grinding angle and honing angle of a plane blade

Honing the sharpening angle of a plane blade to 30° on an oilstone

THINGS TO DO AND THINK ABOUT

1. State what a block plane is used for.

2. State what a bull nose plane is used for.

3. State what a hand router is used for.

4. Describe how you would prevent a hand router cutting below the required depth.

5. State which type of spoke shave you would use to smooth a concave curve.

6. Describe three main stages in sharpening a plane blade.

FLAT-FRAME JOINTING TECHNIQUES

OVERVIEW

Flat-frame construction joints are used to make things like picture frames, mirror frames, window frames and door frames. Within these various frames, you will notice that pieces of wood are joined together using either corner joints, T-joints or crossover joints. By the end of this section on flat-frame joints, you should be able to name and recognise the various types of joints used within each frame and be able to suggest an appropriate joint for a given scenario.

A door frame

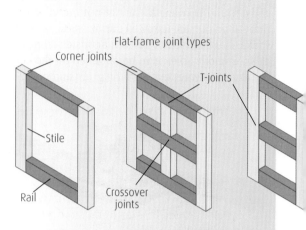

Flat-frame joint types

Corner joints

T-joints

Stile

Rail

Crossover joints

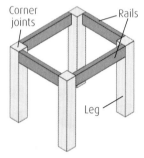

Corner joints

Rails

Leg

Stool, chair and table frame construction

The frames of stools, chairs and tables are made using flat-frame construction joints but each corner has two joints where the rails meet the leg at right angles to each other.

Wooden joints are used to create a bond between two or more pieces of timber. Most timber joints are permanent and are fixed together by wood glue or other fixings. There are many different types of wood joint and it is important that you pick the right one for the job. The joint chosen will depend on a number of factors, such as how strong the joint will have to be, whether the appearance of the joint is important, and how the pieces of wood meet, e.g. do you require a corner joint, T-joint or a crossover joint?

BUTT JOINT

VIDEO LINK

Check out the clip at www.brightredbooks.net to see how to make a bridle joint and how to make a mortise and tenon joint.

This is the most basic wood joint which is only held together by putting glue between the two pieces of wood then allowing them to set while being held together using cramps. It is a very weak joint unless it is strengthened with pins or screws. The butt joint can be used as either a corner or a T-joint. It is mainly used for rough work and construction, for example, basic crates and the eaves of buildings.

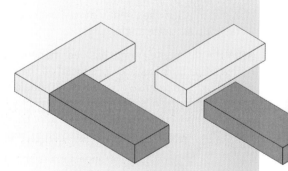

Butt joint: assembled and exploded view

MITRE JOINT

This is also a weak joint unless it is strengthened by nailing into saw cuts across the joint. Mitre joints are neater than butt joints because the end grain is hidden. Mitre joints are typically used for the corners of picture frames and mirror frames.

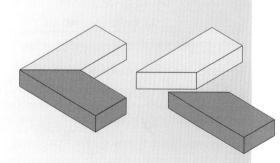

Mitre joint: assembled and exploded view

DOWEL JOINT

Dowel joints tend to be used for lightweight frames. They have replaced many traditional joints in factory-made furniture. For example, when joining rails to legs for a table or chair, it is easier to use dowel joints rather than mortise and tenons. It requires two holes to be drilled into each piece of wood, as shown in the diagram; the dowels are inserted into the drilled holes then the surfaces to be glued are cramped up together. Dowelling jigs are often used to ensure accuracy. The dowels themselves are often made from a hardwood called ramin and come in a range of diameters from 4–25 mm. Just like the butt joint, the dowel joint can be used as either a corner or a T-joint.

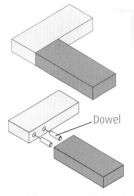
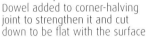

Dowel

Dowel joint: assembled and exploded view

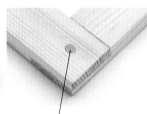

Dowel rod is available in a range of diameters from 4–25 mm

Dowel added to corner-halving joint to strengthen it and cut down to be flat with the surface

CORNER-HALVING JOINT

A corner-halving joint is a quick and easy joint to cut. It is used for lightweight frames and it is often found in door frames, mirror frames and picture frames. Wood of equal thickness is used for both parts of the joint.

Corner-halving joint: assembled and exploded view

CORNER/T-BRIDLE JOINT

Corner bridle joints can be used on frame constructions which will not be subjected to high sideways pressure as this can force the joint out of square. To increase strength, dowels can be inserted through the side of the joint after gluing. It is a strong joint due to its large gluing area and the fact that it can't be twisted apart, unlike the corner-halving joint. Similar to the butt and dowel joints, the corner bridle joint can be adapted to make it suitable for when a T-joint is required (as shown).

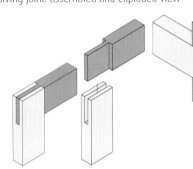

Corner bridle joint: assembled and exploded view

T-bridle joint: assembled and exploded view

✚ DON'T FORGET

When making a bridle joint and mortise and tenon joint, each section of the joint should be a third of the thickness of the piece of wood. It is important to get the thickness of each section right, so as not to weaken the joint.

HAUNCHED MORTISE AND TENON JOINT

Haunched mortise and tenons are often used when joining corners of frames or rails to the ends of legs. The tenon is offset to prevent it breaking through the end grain of the leg or stile. The haunch, which forms a small integral tongue on the tenon, supports the top edge of the rail. It is one of the strongest joints because of its large gluing surface area and crossing of grain. The tenon fits into the mortise and is glued and cramped together.

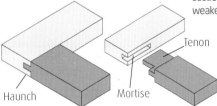

Tenon

Haunch

Mortise

Haunched mortice and tenon joint: assembled and exploded view

THINGS TO DO AND THINK ABOUT

1. Sketch an exploded view of a butt joint, dowel joint, mitre joint, corner-halving joint, corner bridle joint, and a haunched mortise and tenon joint.

2. Name two flat-frame construction joints that are suitable for the corner of a framework.

3. Name two different flat-frame construction joints that are suitable for a T-section of a framework.

4. Describe a method of reinforcing a bridle joint.

 ONLINE TEST

Test yourself on flat-frame jointing techniques at www.brightredbooks.net

MORE FLAT-FRAME JOINTING TECHNIQUES

When a flat frame has a horizontal centre rail or a vertical **muntin**, T- and cross-joints are needed. As we have already seen, some joints, like the butt, dowel and bridle joints, can be used as either a corner or T-joint. In this section, we will look at joints that are specifically used for crossover and T-joints.

DON'T FORGET

You should be able to name and recognise the various types of joints used within each frame and be able to suggest an appropriate joint for a given scenario.

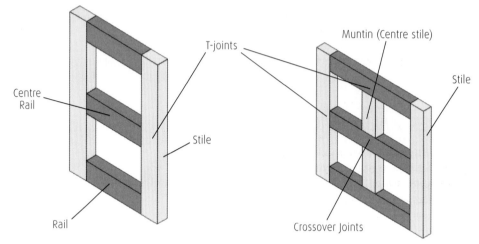

T-joints

Centre Rail

Stile

Rail

Muntin (Centre stile)

Stile

Crossover Joints

Flat-frame joint types

T-HALVING JOINT

The T-halving joint is similar to the corner-halving joint but in this case one of the pieces joins the other in the middle to form a T. They are often found in frame constructions, and due to the surface area where the grain cross, the glued-up joint is reasonably strong. Wood of equal thickness is used for both parts of the joint.

VIDEO LINK

Find out how to make a dovetail template by watching the clip on the Digital Zone.

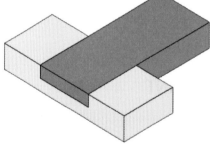

T-halving joint: assembled and exploded view

DON'T FORGET

The dovetail slope is 1:6 for softwood and 1:8 for hardwood. An average slope is 1:7.

DOVETAIL HALVING

Another T-joint, the dovetail halving is one of the most complex joints to make accurately, and as a result it is usually found in expensive quality furniture. Due to its large surface area and the grains crossing it is a strong joint. It has added strength because the dovetail is locked in along its length.

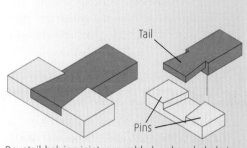

Tail

Pins

Dovetail-halving joint: assembled and exploded view

STUB MORTISE AND TENON JOINT

The stub mortise and tenon, also known as the stopped mortise and tenon, is one of the strongest frame joints and is therefore one of the most frequently used joints on chairs, stools and tables. The main advantage is that once glued up, there are no obvious signs of the joint on the outside of the leg. The depth of the mortise should be about three-quarters of the width of the leg or stile.

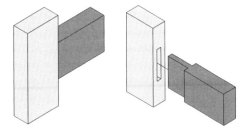

Stub mortise and tenon joint: assembled and exploded view

 DON'T FORGET

Each section of the joint should be a third of the thickness of the piece of wood. It is important to get the thickness of each section right, so as not to weaken the joint.

THROUGH MORTISE AND TENON JOINT

The through mortise and tenon is very similar to the stub mortise and tenon, except this time the tenon goes all the way through the width of the leg or stile (as shown). This type of T-joint is, again, a very strong joint, but can be strengthened further by inserting a wedge into the end of the tenon once the tenon is in place. This joint is often used to join the middle rail to the stiles when making a door frame.

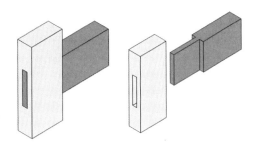

Through mortise and tenon joint: assembled and exploded view

A wedge inserted into a through mortise and tenon to increase its strength

CROSS-HALVING JOINT

Cross-halving joints are often found in frame constructions where you have a rail and a centre stile crossing over each other. Wood of equal thickness is used for both parts of the joint and half the timber of the joint is removed from each piece of wood – hence the name halving joint. It's quite a strong joint and it takes practice to make it fit well. It can be used on door frames and window frames due to the joint being flat on both sides.

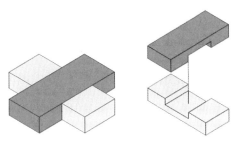

Cross-halving joint: assembled and exploded view

 VIDEO LINK

Find out how to make a wooden gate at www.brightredbooks.net

 THINGS TO DO AND THINK ABOUT

1. Sketch an exploded view of a T-halving joint, dovetail-halving joint, through mortise and tenon joint and a cross-halving joint.

2. Suggest a reason for using a dovetail-halving joint rather than a T-halving joint in the manufacture of a flat frame.

3. Describe a method of reinforcing a through mortise and tenon joint.

4. Suggest the recommended dovetail slope that could be used when making a dovetail halving from hardwood.

 ONLINE TEST

Take the test on crossover flat-frame jointing techniques at www.brightredbooks.net

CARCASE CONSTRUCTION FRAME TECHNIQUES

Carcase construction, sometimes known as box construction, refers to a wide range of box-shaped frames such as a simple butt jointed pencil holder, to more complicated furniture like bookcases and wardrobes. Each of these frames will contain corner joints of some sort and perhaps a T-joint. You would include a T-joint when a cabinet contains a shelf, for example, in a bookcase, or when a box has several compartments, such as in a cutlery tray.

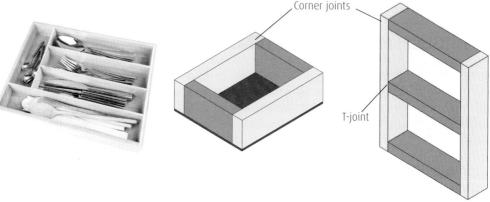

Carcase construction joint types

This section starts off by looking at simple carcase joints, before moving on to the more advanced joints that are used in the construction of various carcase frames.

As with the flat frame construction section, you should be able to name and recognise the various types of joints used within each carcase frame and be able to suggest an appropriate joint for a given scenario.

BUTT JOINT

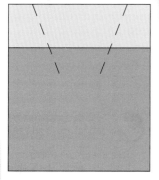

Example of dovetail nailing

Butt joints are the quickest and simplest to make. It's a weak joint as it's only held together with glue. A butt joint can be reinforced using nails. For the greatest strength and to reduce the chances of the joint being pulled apart, the nails are best used in pairs and put into the wood angled towards each other. This is known as **dovetail nailing** and is shown (left). A butt joint tends to be used for rough work or when the strength of the joint isn't of great importance to the product, for example a lightweight crate. Butt joints can be used to create corners or T-joints for partitions within carcase construction frames.

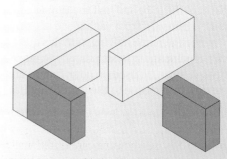

Butt joint: assembled and exploded view

CORNER REBATE JOINT

Corner rebate joints, also known as lap joints, are stronger than butt joints because they increase the area being glued and are neater because less end grain is shown. Like the butt joint, it relies on glue and nails for its strength. A corner rebate is used to join wood at corners, for example, the corner of a drawer or a box.

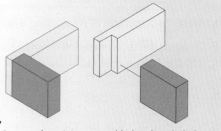

Corner rebate joint: assembled and exploded view

DOWEL JOINT

Dowel joints are quick and easy to make and tend to be used for light-to-medium weight frames. They have replaced many traditional joints in factory-made furniture. It only requires two holes to be drilled into each piece of wood, as shown in the diagram; the dowels are inserted into the drilled holes then the surfaces to be glued are cramped up together. Dowelling jigs are often used to ensure accuracy. The dowels themselves are often made from a hardwood called ramin and come in a range of diameters from 4–25 mm. Just like the butt joint, the dowel joint can be used as either a corner or a T-joint.

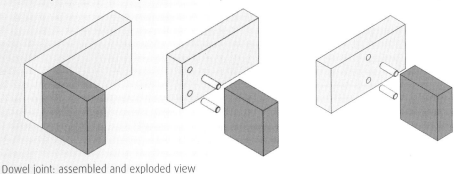

Dowel joint: assembled and exploded view

HOUSING JOINTS

Housing joints are very strong and are used solely when a T-joint is required, for example, when a cabinet or box includes shelves or a partition. The two types of housing joint are a through housing joint and a stopped housing joint.

 VIDEO LINK

Watch the clip about how to make a housing joint at www.brightredbooks.net

THROUGH HOUSING JOINT

Through housings are easier to cut than stopped housings because they are cut across the whole width of the board. The main disadvantage with the though housing over the stopped housing is you can see where the two pieces of wood join.

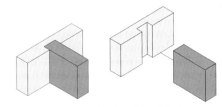

Housing joint: assembled and exploded view

STOPPED HOUSING JOINT

The stopped housing is harder to make, but is neater in appearance than the through housing. Stopped housings are traditionally found in quality furniture mainly due to their strength and the fact that you cannot see the joint from the front.

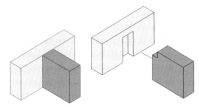

Stopped housing joint: assembled and exploded view

 THINGS TO DO AND THINK ABOUT

1. Sketch an exploded view of a corner rebate joint, through housing joint, and a stopped housing joint.
2. Suggest a reason for using a stopped housing joint rather than a through housing joint in the manufacture of a bookshelf.
3. Describe a method of reinforcing a butt joint.
4. Name two carcase construction joints that are suitable for the corner of a framework.
5. Name two different carcase construction joints that are suitable for T-sections of a framework.

 ONLINE TEST

Test yourself on carcase frame techniques at www.brightredbooks.net

MECHANICAL FIXING AND ADHESIVE BONDING

MECHANICAL FIXING AND ADHESIVE BONDING

KNOCK DOWN FIXINGS

Many items of furniture you will find around your home such as kitchen cabinets and wardrobes have been designed so that they can be joined together or taken apart quickly and easily at home. This type of self-assembly furniture is known as flat-pack furniture and is commonly made from manufactured board and joined together using various mechanical fixings known as knock down fixings. Some commonly used knock down fixings are shown below.

Corner block

A corner block is one of the most basic knock down fixings used in self-assembly furniture. It provides a strong, cheap and effective method of joining two pieces of wood together at right angles. Although the example in the picture shows a plastic corner block, it could quite easily have been made from a piece of natural timber such as pine having holes drilled into it then screwed into place.

A barrel and bolt joint is one of the strongest knock down fixings and can be taken apart and reassembled quickly and easily. Typically found in self-assembly tables, the barrel and bolt joint is assembled by inserting the bolt through both components to be joined together where it locates the threaded hole in the barrel, and it is then tightened up by an Allen key. As it's tightened, the two components are pulled together to achieve a very strong joint.

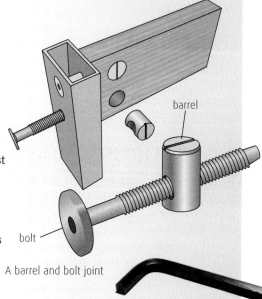

barrel

bolt

A barrel and bolt joint

Allen key

One of the strongest, most complex knock down fixings is the cam lock fixing. Commonly found in self-assembly kitchen cabinets, this fixing uses a specialist screw which is tightened into one component then inserted into the second component where the head of the screw is located in the cam. The cam is then tightened by a screwdriver, which in turn pulls the two components together.

A basic and easy to assemble and disassemble knock down fixing is the furniture screw connector. As the name suggests, this is commonly used in the assembly of flat-pack furniture. Its deep thread provides an accurate, close-fitting joint in the manufactured board where normal wood screws could easily tear out.

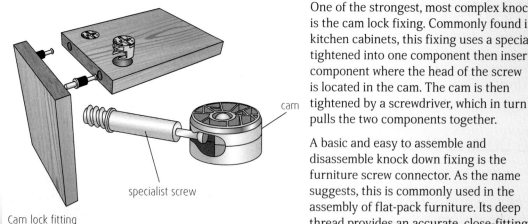

cam

specialist screw

Cam lock fitting

Furniture screw connector

Angle brackets are commonly used as a structural support for reinforcing right-angle corner joints. It's a simple method of joining materials together, and just like the corner block it is held in position using screws, meaning it can be taken apart and reassembled quickly and easily. Some typical uses for an angle bracket would be attaching a table top to the table frames and fixing kitchen units to a wall.

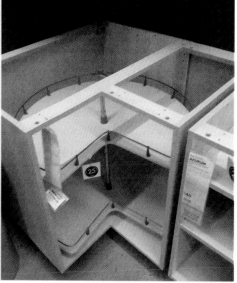

Angle brackets

An angle bracket in use

A kitchen cabinet assembled using knock down fixings

Advantages of flat-pack furniture

Self-assembly, flat-pack furniture which is joined together using knock down fixings has many advantages over traditional woodworking techniques:

VIDEO LINK

Find out how to use an angle bracket by watching the clip at www.brightredbooks.net

- It's cheaper to manufacture as consumers assemble it themselves.

- It's made from manufactured board, rather than natural timber, which is better for the environment.

- It's quick and easy to assemble and take apart using limited specialist equipment – often just a screwdriver or an Allen key is required.

- It's easier to transport and deliver; for example, large furniture items such as wardrobes and dining room tables, which are awkward to handle and manoeuvre around a house when they're assembled, can be assembled in the room where they will be used.

Flat-pack furniture being assembled

WOOD ADHESIVE

Unlike knock down fixings, traditional wood joints are assembled using wood glue. The most commonly used wood glue in schools is PVA glue. PVA (polyvinyl-acetate) glue is a thick, white, water-based glue which is supplied in a bottle with a thin nozzle that allows the glue to be applied right into the corners of the joints. Unlike superglue, which has a very short setting time, PVA will take around 3–4 hours to dry and set to a strong, permanent joint. Traditionally, PVA glue is used for interior applications; however, if a product is going to come into contact with water or is required for exterior use, an exterior grade waterproof PVA glue should be used.

PVA glue

DON'T FORGET

To prevent any excess glue staining the surface of your wood, you should remove it immediately using a damp paper towel.

THINGS TO DO AND THINK ABOUT

1. State two pieces of furniture you may find around your home that had been designed as self-assembly, flat-packed furniture.
2. Flat-packed furniture is commonly assembled using knock down fixings. State the name of three different knock down fixings that are available for use.
3. State two advantages of using knock down fixings over traditional wood joint techniques.
4. State why a bottle of PVA glue is fitted with a thin nozzle.
5. State when an exterior grade of PVA glue should be considered for use.

ONLINE TEST

Test yourself on mechanical fixing and adhesive bonding on the Digital Zone.

THE SAFE USE OF CRAMPING DEVICES

HOLDING DEVICES

Whether you require to hold a workpiece securely in place while cutting, drilling or chiselling, or you need to hold an assembled model under pressure while the glue is setting, you will need to use some sort of holding device. A well-equipped workshop will have a collection of cramps, often called clamps, to meet each of these operations. A selection of commonly used cramps is shown below.

Sash Cramps

The sash cramp is used when large boxes or frames such as door or window frames are assembled. Sash cramps have a capacity of 450mm to 2m.

Parts of a sash cramp

A sash cramp in use

To adjust a sash cramp when gluing up a frame, the back jaw rests against the locking pin which is in one of the holes that run along the bar of the cramp, and the head jaw is screwed into place using the tommy bar to tighten the head jaw securely against the frame to hold it in place.

G-Cramp

The G-cramp is used to hold a workpiece securely in place while cutting, drilling or chiselling, and to hold glued components together while the glue sets. G-cramps have a capacity of 50–350mm.

Mitre Cramp

The mitre cramp is mainly used to cramp up mitre joints in picture frames and trinket boxes. It's designed in such a way that the jaws of the cramp hold the joint in place at an exact angle of 90°.

Although the main use of the mitre cramp is to cramp up mitre joints for picture frames, it can also be used to cramp other joints at 90°, like the dowel joints in the bookshelf shown below.

A picture frame with mitre joints

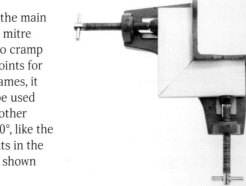

Mitre cramp in use

G-Cramp

contd

Band Cramp

Band cramps use large straps and corner brackets to hold large, irregular frames in place and apply pressure while the glue has time to set. As the straps are tightened, they provide a uniformly distributed amount of pressure equally around the frame, which helps to prevent any distortion in the frame.

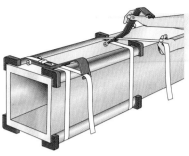

String and Block

The string and block technique of cramping up frames is very similar to the band cramp technique. Wooden blocks are placed at each corner of the frame then a length of string is wrapped around the frame. Then the string is tied in a knot to apply even pressure on each corner all the way around the frame.

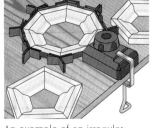

An example of an irregular-shaped picture frame cramped up using band cramps

VIDEO LINK

Watch the video at www.brightredbooks.net to see how the large carcase frame is cramped up using a band cramp.

DRY CRAMPING

One of the most important stages of assembling any model is to **dry cramp** it. Dry cramping is when you cramp up your model without applying any glue. The purpose of dry cramping is to make sure that all the joints fit together properly and there are no mistakes before applying the glue. It also gives you an opportunity to check you have all the required cramps set up in the correct position and that they are in good working order.

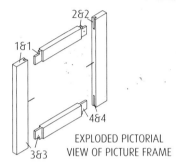

EXPLODED PICTORIAL VIEW OF PICTURE FRAME

Label each joint in preparation for assembling your frame

DON'T FORGET

In preparation for dry cramping your frame, it's a good idea to number each joint in the frame to make sure you pair up the correct rail to its corresponding stile.

CHECKING FOR SQUARENESS

Once you have dry cramped your model, as well as checking all the joints fit together properly, you should check the assembly for **squareness**. There are two main techniques for checking the assembly for squareness and they are shown below.

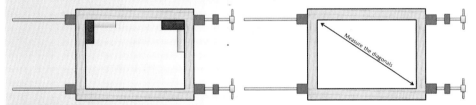

Checking for squareness:

- A try square should be placed in each corner to check all corners are at 90°.
- Measure the distance between the diagonals. If both diagonals are the same, the frame is square.

THINGS TO DO AND THINK ABOUT

1. State two adjustments that can be made to a sash cramp.
2. When a cramp is tightened, it could damage the edge of your workpiece. Describe how this damage could be avoided.
3. State two uses for a G-cramp.
4. State which type of cramp could be used for an irregular-shaped frame.
5. Explain what is meant by the term "dry cramping".
6. State a reason for numbering each joint in a frame.
7. After a frame is cramped up, it should be checked for squareness. State two methods of checking for squareness.

ONLINE TEST

Test your knowledge of cramping on the Digital Zone.

WOODTURNING LATHE 1

VIDEO LINK

Learn more about turning a spinning top by watching a clip on the Digital Zone.

Lampstand

Wooden staircase with turned spindles

Candle holder

A wooden pen

VIDEO LINK

Watch the clip about turning a rolling pin at www.brightredbooks.net

LATHE PARTS AND TYPES OF TURNING

Lathe Parts

A wood lathe is a fixed machine used to turn cylindrical shapes from a solid piece of wood using a variety of tools and chisels. As you can see from the picture below, it's quite a basic machine, comprising four main parts, the headstock, tool rest, tailstock and the lathe bed.

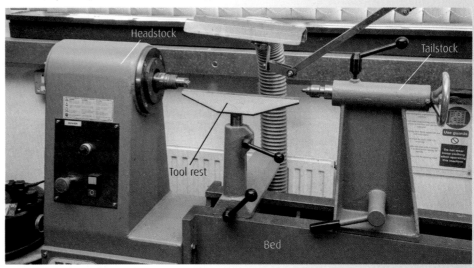

Parts of the wood lathe

The fixed headstock houses the motor which provides the drive to spin the wood.

The adjustable tool rest is used to support the lathe tool while shaping the wood.

The tool rest can be adjusted in four main directions:

- Up and down to position the height of the tool rest to allow the blade of the turning tool to be supported just above or below the centre axis of the wood that is secured in the lathe. The height the tool rest is set to is determined by the tool being used and the process being carried out.
- Left and right along the lathe bed to allow for varying lengths of wood.
- Forwards and backwards across the lathe bed to accommodate wood of varying diameters.
- The angle to the centre line of the lathe to suit the tool being used and the process that is being carried out, for example, taper turning.

The tailstock is also moveable and can be moved left and right along the lathe bed to accommodate varying lengths of wood.

Types of Turning

There are two different types of turning: turning between centres and face-plate turning. Turning between centres is used to turn things like lampstands, rolling pins and spindles for staircases, whereas face-plate turning is mainly used to turn things like bowls and serving platters. Examples of products that have been turned between centres are shown.

 contd

Turning between Centres

When turning between centres, the blank of wood is held in place between two centres. On the left-hand side, attached to the head stock, is the forked centre, and on the right-hand side, attached to the tailstock, you either have a revolving centre or a dead centre. In the set-up shown below, a wooden blank is held in place between a forked centre and a revolving centre.

A wooden blank being held in place between two centres

Forked centre attached to the headstock

Revolving centre fits into the tailstock

The Centres

When turning between centres, it is the two centres that are holding the wooden blank at either end while the wood is spinning.

The forked centre, which is attached to the head stock, provides the drive to spin the wooden blank at a suitable speed.

The revolving centre serves two purposes: it supports the other end of the wooden blank and rotates with the wood. Whereas the dead centre, as the name suggests, does not rotate with the wood, and its only function is to hold the wood in place. The disadvantage of using a dead centre over a revolving centre is that the dead centre causes friction between the blank and the centre and, as a result, will cause the end of the wood to wear, generate heat and burn. To reduce any burning, lubricant can be applied to the end of the blank that is being supported by the dead centre.

Forked centre

Revolving centre

PREPARING A BLANK FOR TURNING BETWEEN CENTRES

Prior to turning a blank of wood on the wood lathe, you must first prepare the wood to allow it to be held securely in place between the two centres. To do this, you should follow these four main stages.

Dead centre

Stage 1

Using a steel rule, mark diagonals on both ends to locate the centre.

Stage 2

Using a hammer and a centre punch, create an indent in both ends to allow the centres to be located.

Stage 3

Using a tenon saw, cut a groove to accommodate the forked centre.

Stage 4

Using a smoothing plane, remove the corners of the blank to make the initial stage of turning a cylinder easier.

The prepared wooden blank

THINGS TO DO AND THINK ABOUT

1. Draw a diagram of a wood lathe and label the four main parts.
2. The tool rest can be adjusted in three different ways. Describe the three adjustments that can be made and a possible reason for each adjustment.
3. The tailstock can also be adjusted. Describe how it can be adjusted and a possible reason for the adjustment.
4. State the purpose of the forked centre.
5. State a reason for using a revolving centre rather than a dead centre.
6. Describe the four main stages to follow when preparing a blank to be turned between centres.
7. State four wooden products that could be made by turning between centres.

WOODTURNING LATHE 2

Forked centre

Forked centre attached to the headstock

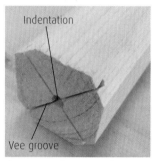
Indentation

Vee groove

The prepared, octagonal-shaped, wooden blank

SETTING UP THE LATHE FOR TURNING BETWEEN CENTRES

Once the wooden blank is prepared for the lathe, it is time to mount the blank onto the lathe. To do this, four stages should be followed.

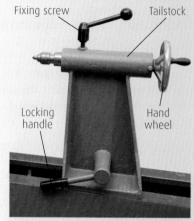
Fixing screw — Tailstock

Locking handle — Hand wheel

Parts of the tailstock labelled

Stage 1

Line up the vee groove and the indentation on the blank with the forked centre, then tap the other end of the blank with a mallet.

Stage 2

To secure the wooden blank in place, the tailstock, with either a revolving centre or dead centre, is moved into position and locked using the locking handle.

Stage 3

Slacken the fixing screw, then turn the hand wheel to make fine adjustments to the position of the revolving/dead centre before tightening the fixing screw.

Stage 4

Adjust the tool rest into position then lock securely in place.

Excess material at either end of the wooden blank to allow the damage caused by the centres to be cut off

Turned blank mounted on a wood lathe

TURNING TOOLS AND PROFILES

Most workpieces will start off as a prepared octagonal blank which should then be turned to produce a regular cylinder as shown. Once the blank is uniformly shaped into a cylinder, various cylindrical forms can be created using four different lathe tools: gouge, parting chisel, skew chisel and scraper.

vee groove   shoulder   hollow   bobbin

Common forms created while wood turning

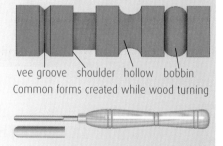
Gouge

Gouge

The gouge is a good general purpose lathe tool. There are two main types of gouge, the roughing gouge and the spindle gouge. It's the roughing gouge that is commonly used for removing waste material quickly (roughing); for example, to turn the blank from its octagonal shape into a cylindrical shape. The thinner spindle gouge is used for more intricate details such as concave curves like the hollow shown (right).

Creating a concave curve using a spindle gouge

Skew Chisel

The skew chisel is used to cut various intricate, detailed cuts into the wooden blank such as vee grooves and bobbins.

Skew chisel

Parting Chisel

As the name suggests, one of the main uses of the parting chisel is to separate the finished work from the waste material. It can also be used to create square shoulders and steps.

Parting chisel

Scraper

Although a scraper can be used like the gouge to remove waste material and create a basic cylindrical shape, it is mainly used to create a smooth surface prior to sanding. It can also be used to create concave curves, such as hollows.

Scraper

Creating a bobbin shape using a skew chisel

Creating a square shoulder with a parting tool

Tool Handling

As you can see from the picture, lathe tools come with long handles. This is for two reasons, to achieve a good grip of the tool handle and to allow good leverage.

Working to a given Diameter and a specified Length

As you work through the course, you will be expected to provide evidence that you can turn a workpiece to a given diameter and to specified lengths stated in a working drawing and/or to match a template to a tolerance of ±1 mm. An example of a turnery template is shown below.

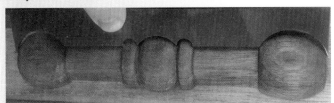
Turnery template being used to check a turnery piece matches the template

A scraper being used to create a cylindrical shape: with the handle pointing downwards, being held firmly, with both hands, against the tool rest

Faceplate Turning

The other basic type of turning carried out on a wood lathe is faceplate turning. The most common type of wood turning projects produced on a faceplate are wooden bowls and serving platters. Just like turning between centres, the solid piece of wood to be turned needs to be prepared prior to it being mounted onto the lathe. To prepare the wood for faceplate turning, the wood is cut into an octagonal shape. The faceplate is positioned centrally onto the wood and is fixed in place with wood screws. The final stage is to attach the faceplate directly onto the spindle of the head stock.

A faceplate used to turn a wooden bowl

 THINGS TO DO AND THINK ABOUT

1. Describe the four main stages to follow when mounting a blank, to be turned between centres, onto the wood lathe.
2. State the name of a turning tool used to turn a wooden blank from its octagonal shape into a cylindrical shape.
3. State the name of a turning tool used to create vee grooves and bobbins on a workpiece.
4. State the name of a turning tool used to create square shoulders on a workpiece.
5. State two wooden products that could be made by faceplate turning.

A wooden bowl attached to a faceplate

MACHINES: PILLAR DRILL AND DRILL BITS

PILLAR DRILL

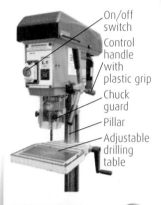

On/off switch

Control handle with plastic grip

Chuck guard

Pillar

Adjustable drilling table

The pillar drill, also known as the pedestal drill, is a heavy duty drilling machine used for drilling round holes in wood, metal and plastic. It is the best way to consistently drill straight holes (at 90° to the surface) accurately. In the pictures shown, you will find the main parts of the drill clearly labelled. You should familiarise yourself with these terms and their location.

Pillar drills come in a variety of sizes; this large pillar drill stands on the floor; however, smaller ones are available and may be secured to a bench. The main advantage of having a large pillar drill is that the adjustable drilling table can be moved up or down the pillar to allow pieces of wood of various lengths to be drilled vertically.

No matter what material you are drilling or what drill bit you are using, the drill bit must be secured in the chuck by tightening it with the chuck key.

Chuck

To change a drill bit, the chuck key is inserted into one of the holes in the chuck and is then turned to loosen or tighten the jaws around the drill bit. The jaw-opening range is 1–13 mm.

Control handle

Depth stop

Depth Stop

Occasionally you will need to drill a **blind hole** in a piece of material. A blind hole refers to a hole that has been drilled to a specified depth without breaking through to the other side of the material. To ensure that the drill bit will only drill down to a specific depth, you will need to set the **depth stop**.

If a hole is to be drilled all the way through a piece of wood, it is good practice to place a piece of waste wood underneath it to prevent the workpiece splitting when the drill bit breaks through.

It is very important that your workpiece is held securely in place while drilling. Larger pieces of wood should be clamped to the drilling table using a G-clamp and smaller pieces of wood that are to be drilled can be held in place using a machine vice.

DRILL BITS

Twist Drill

One of the drill bits that you will use most often is the twist drill. A twist drill is used to drill small holes in all materials and can be used in either hand, power or machine drills.

Flutes (for removing the waste material)   Shank

Twist drill

When you are securing a twist drill into the chuck, you should always make sure that the drill bit is located centrally between the jaws of the chuck and that the jaws are closed onto the straight shank of the drill bit, and not the fluted section. This set-up will ensure that the twist drill is fixed firmly in the chuck and that the drill bit will turn true (and not wobble).

Common twist drill sizes are 1–13 mm in 0.5 mm increments.

Chuck

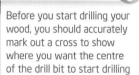

Chuck key

Chuck and chuck key

Countersink Rose

A countersink rose creates a chamfer in the entrance to a drilled hole, allowing a countersunk screw head to go level or slightly below the surface of the material. A countersink rose can be used in wood, metal or plastic using either a hand, power or machine drill.

A common size for a countersink rose is up to 13 mm with a 6–8 mm shank.

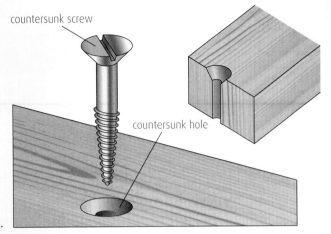
countersunk screw
countersunk hole

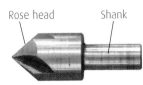
Rose head   Shank
Countersink rose

Forstner Bit

A forstner bit is a specialist drill bit used to bore clean, accurate **flat-bottomed holes**. It comes into its own when you need to bore half a hole on the edge of a board or overlapping holes. It is unaffected by knots and awkward grain in wood, and for best results, it should be used in a pillar drill.

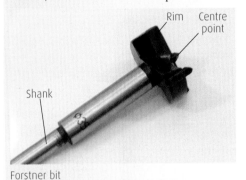
Rim   Centre point
Shank
Forstner bit

A flat bottom hole created using a forstner bit

A forstner bit can be used to bore half a hole on the edge of a board

Common forstner bit sizes are 10–50 mm, with shanks of around 10 mm at the top to fit into the chuck of a drill.

Flat Bit

A flat bit is designed to be used in a power tool to drill large holes in natural wood or manufactured board.

Common flat bit sizes are 6–32 mm, with shanks of around 10 mm at the top to fit into the chuck of a drill.

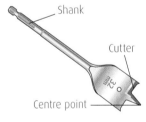
Shank
Cutter
Centre point
Flat bit

THINGS TO DO AND THINK ABOUT

1. What is the pillar drill also known as?

2. Suggest a reason why the drilling table can be adjusted up and down the pillar.

3. Name the tool that should be used to hold large pieces of wood in place while drilling.

4. Suggest how you could prevent your wood from splitting on the underside when a hole is to be drilled all the way through it.

5. State which drill bit is used to produce flat-bottomed holes.

6. Produce a sketch and label the main parts of a twist drill, countersink rose, forstner bit and a flat bit.

ONLINE TEST

Test yourself on pillar drills at www.brightredbooks.net

MACHINES: MORTISE MACHINE, BELT SANDER AND DISC SANDER

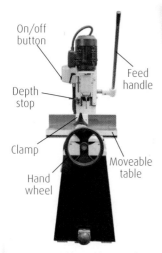

On/off button

Feed handle

Depth stop

Clamp

Hand wheel

Moveable table

Main parts of a mortise machine

VIDEO LINK

Learn how to set up and use a mortise machine by watching the video on the Digital Zone.

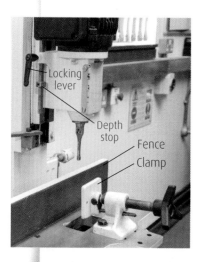

Locking lever

Depth stop

Fence

Clamp

DON'T FORGET

The depth stop should be set to ensure the mortise is accurately cut down to the required depth.

MORTISE MACHINE

A mortise machine makes the square holes required for the mortise part of a mortise and tenon joint. Although mortises are traditionally cut using a mortise chisel and mallet, it's quicker and easier to use a mortise machine.

Positioning and Securing the Workpiece

As when using any machine, the workpiece being worked on should be held firmly in place. In the case of the mortise machine, the workpiece is positioned against the fence then secured in place using the clamp. To prevent the clamp from marking the workpiece while it is being tightened, it's good practice to place a piece of scrap wood between the clamp and the workpiece.

Setting the Depth

The bit is secured into the chisel headstock then lowered down onto the wood by pulling the feed handle towards you. To help with setting the depth of cut made by the bit, if it's not a through mortise, it's a good idea to mark out the required mortise depth onto the end grain of the work piece.

Stage 1: Slacken the locking lever.

Stage 2: Using the feed handle, lower the bit until the lowest part of the bit meets the depth line.

Stage 3: Tighten up the locking lever.

For a through mortise, the workpiece should be supported on a piece of scrap wood and the depth of cut can be set using the same method as above.

Cutting a Mortise

The square hole is cut using a mortise bit. Different lengths of mortises can be cut by the square mortise bit by adjusting the movable table left or right by using the hand wheel.

Stage 1: With the mortise marked out on the workpiece, clamp the wood firmly against the fence and onto the moveable table.

Stage 2: Using the feed handle, lower the bit onto the workpiece to check it is aligned with the mortise to be cut. Using the hand wheel, the table can be moved forward or backward to line up the chisel with your markings.

Stage 3: Set the depth stop.

Stage 4: Turn on the machine, starting at one end of the mortise; lower the bit down to cut to the required depth before slowly working along the length of the mortise. As you work along the mortise, take out one square slot out at a time, making sure to stop precisely on the other end of the mortise line.

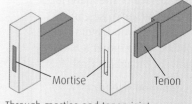

Mortise

Tenon

Through mortise and tenon joint: assembled and exploded view

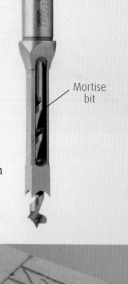

Mortise bit

Mortise marked out ready to be cut

SANDING MACHINES

VIDEO LINK

Check out the clip on the Digital Zone to see a belt sander in action.

As you work your way through the Practical Woodworking course, it is likely that you will use a sanding machine. Sanding machines are available in various forms: the most common are the belt sander and the disc sander. An example of each type of sanding machine is shown below.

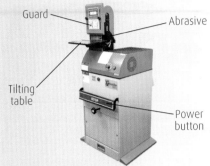

Guard — Abrasive — Tilting table — Power button

Main parts of a belt sander

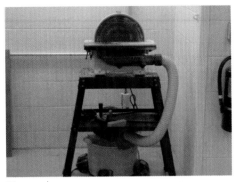

Disc sander

Sanding a piece of wood down to a line

No matter which type of sanding machine your school workshop has, its main purpose is shaping and finishing wood. A sanding machine can very quickly and easily sand a straight piece of wood down to a line, smooth a convex curve, or create a bevel/chamfer on a piece of wood.

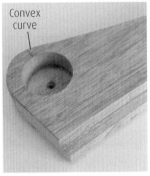

Convex curve

A convex curve shaped on the sanding machine

Safety in Use

A sanding machine is a simple machine to use. However, as with any machine, care must be taken when using it.

- Do not wear loose clothing, neck ties or jewellery that can become entangled with the sanding belt.
- Wear eye protection.
- Familiarise yourself with the emergency stop buttons prior to using the machine.
- Ensure the guard is in place and set to an appropriate level for the workpiece being sanded.
- Ensure the workpiece is resting on the table when sanding.
- After turning the sanding machine on, make sure the belt/disc is running freely prior to gently moving the workpiece into contact with the sanding belt/disc.
- Always make sure you keep your hands clear from the moving belt/disc.
- Never distract or talk to someone who is using a machine.
- Always switch off the sanding machine when it's not in use.

The table can be tilted to create a chamfer

THINGS TO DO AND THINK ABOUT

1. State a reason for using a mortise machine to cut mortises rather than the more traditional method of using a mortise chisel and mallet.
2. Describe the process of setting the depth on a mortise machine.
3. Describe the process of cutting a mortise using a mortise machine.
4. Give the names of the two main types of sanding machines found in a school workshop.
5. State the purpose of using a sanding machine.
6. State three processes that can be carried out using a sanding machine.
7. State four safety rules that should be observed while using a sanding machine.

VIDEO LINK

Find out how to use a belt sander by watching the clip at www.brightredbooks.net

ONLINE TEST

Test yourself on this topic at www.brightredbooks.net

POWER TOOLS

ONLINE

Head to the Digital Zone for additional videos and activities on power tools!

Corded drill in use

A cordless drill being used

DON'T FORGET

Always select the correct screwdriver bit for the screw being used. This will ensure the bit does not damage or strip the head of the screw or jump out and damage the surface of the workpiece.

DRILLS

Corded Drill

A corded drill is powered by plugging it directly into the mains power supply. With that in mind, care must be taken to prevent the cord becoming a tripping hazard. Its main use is to drill holes in a whole range of materials including wood, metal and brickwork. The drill shown is fitted with a safety, keyless chuck. This means a drill bit can be changed simply by turning the chuck in opposite directions to open the chuck.

Cordless Drill

A truly portable power tool, the cordless drill is battery-powered and can be used to quickly and easily drill holes in a variety of materials. Just like the corded drill, the cordless drill is fitted with a self-locking chuck. Not only is the cordless drill lighter than the corded drill, but the potential tripping hazard is also avoided.

Cordless Screwdriver

Although some cordless drills can be used for inserting screws, a purpose-built cordless screwdriver is available. These power tools come into their own when several screws require to be fixed into place. One of the most common issues with using a cordless drill/screwdriver to fix a screw in place is overtightening the screw or stripping the screw head. The adjustable torque selection setting helps ensure that you do not strip the head of the screw as the screw is tightened. Care must also be taken to select the screwdriver bit that is the correct size for the screw head being used. The standardised octagonal shape of the bits make them quick and easy to be changed to suit a variety of screw heads.

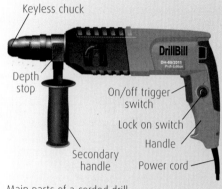

Main parts of a corded drill

Main parts of a cordless drill

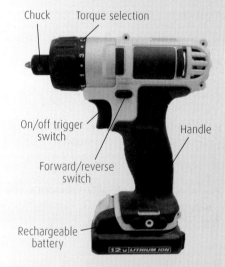

Main parts of a cordless screwdriver.

An example of the various bits available for use in a cordless drill/screwdriver

A screw being driven in by a cordless screwdriver

JIG SAW

The jig saw is a versatile portable saw which can be used for cutting both straight and complex curved cuts in either thin sheets or thicker boards. When an accurate straight cut is required, a fence can be attached to the side of the base plate to ensure the saw blade stays parallel to the edge of the material. When the correct blade is used, a jig saw will easily cut through a variety of materials such as plywood, chipboard, blockboard, and even thin metals.

Jig saws cut on the upwards stoke. With that in mind, to reduce the possibility of chipping the surface of the face of the workpiece, clamp the workpiece firmly in place, face downwards.

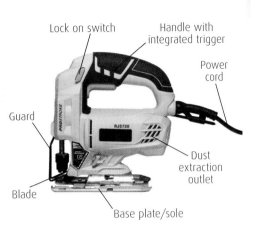

Lock on switch — Handle with integrated trigger — Power cord — Guard — Blade — Base plate/sole — Dust extraction outlet

Main parts of a jig saw

Jigsaw blade

DON'T FORGET

The workpiece firmly clamped to bench with the blade able to move freely without cutting the work bench or the power cord

PORTABLE SANDERS

Orbital Sander

The orbital sander is a power sander used with a fine abrasive paper to achieve a smooth finish on a wooden surface prior to applying a finish. This is much easier than manually hand-sanding wood and is particularly useful for large jobs such as table tops or panels. The abrasive paper, which is cut to the specific shape of the orbital sander, can be attached to the base plate with hook and loop backing, or by using the abrasive paper clips. An orbital sander should be held flat on the surface, and with an even, steady pressure being applied, it should be worked back and forth along the grain. Any movement across the grain of the wood can leave circular scratches on the surface of the wood.

Belt Sander

The belt sander is designed for more heavy duty sanding on large surfaces. It will remove waste fast, although by working through the various abrasive grades, coarse, medium and fine, a smooth surface can be achieved.

Lock on switch — Handle with integrated trigger — Power cord — Front handle — Dust extraction outlet — Abrasive paper clip — Abrasive paper attached — Base plate — Abrasive paper clip

Main parts of an orbital sander

Power cord — Dust filter box — Handle with integrated trigger — Belt-release — Abrasive paper

Main parts of a belt sander

A typical sanding belt

THINGS TO DO AND THINK ABOUT

1. State the advantage of a drill being fitted with a keyless chuck.
2. State a safety precaution which should be observed while using a corded drill.
3. Describe how to prevent stripping the head of a screw while using a cordless screwdriver to fix a screw in place.
4. Describe how an accurate straight cut could be achieved using a jig saw.
5. State a safety precaution which should be observed while using a jig saw.
6. Describe how to avoid creating scratches on the surface of a table top when using an orbital sander to prepare it for a finish to be applied.

ONLINE TEST

Test yourself on this topic on the Digital Zone.

SURFACE PREPARATION TECHNIQUES

WOOD PREPARATION TECHNIQUES

Most products that are made from wood require a finish to be applied. Applying a finish to a product will not only make it look better but make it last longer. Before applying a finish to a product, its surfaces must be cleaned up and smoothed down. This basic preparation is a very important stage of the finishing process, and although sometimes it is tempting to rush this stage of the process, a poorly prepared surface will be highlighted and becomes more noticeable once a finish is applied.

This chapter will look at the various preparation techniques that can and should be followed to ensure that a smooth surface, free from defects, is achieved ready for a high-quality finish to be applied.

A well-prepared surface should have:

- all pencil marks removed
- no evidence of glue marks
- no scratch marks from abrasives
- all imperfections that have been left after machining the wood removed.

Scraper

A smoothing plane can be used to give a clean smooth surface, although a scraper may be required for difficult hardwoods where the grain is interlocked, or where there are knots. A scraper is a very simple tool to use. The blade which is ground on the long edge of the scraper is placed on the wood, and with pressure applied to the centre of the scraper with your thumbs, it is pushed away from you along the wood, removing fine shavings as it goes.

VIDEO LINK

Check out the wood preparation tutorial at www.brightredbooks.net

Scraper being used to clean up a piece of hardwood

A pair of scrapers

Wood stopping and wood filler can both be applied using a filling knife. Once dried, the filler should be sanded down to leave a smooth surface

Wood Stopping

Wood stopping is a natural, solvent-based wood pulp used for filling holes, cracks and gaps in unfinished wood. It is quick drying and can be drilled and sanded when dry. It is available in a wide range of colours and it is important to select the colour that is closest to the colour of the wood.

Wood Filler

Wood filler is a water-based filler used to fill and repair surface damage to wood. It is quick-drying and can be drilled and sanded when dry. Wood filler is suitable for both interior and exterior use and can be stained, waxed or varnished. Just like wood stopper, it is available in a wide range of colours and it is important to select the colour that is closest to the colour of the wood.

ABRASIVE PAPER

Abrasive Types

Although abrasive paper is commonly referred to as sandpaper, the two main types of abrasive paper used for woodworking are glass paper and garnet paper. Glass paper consists of pieces of crushed glass glued onto a backing paper, whereas garnet paper consists of pieces of crushed natural hard-wearing stone glued onto backing paper – and is therefore longer lasting. Compared with garnet paper, glass paper is softer and relatively inexpensive.

Abrasive paper

DON'T FORGET

When it's a deeper hole that is to be repaired, this may need to be built up in layers.

Abrasive Grades

Both glass paper and garnet paper are available in a range of grades: fine, medium and coarse. Abrasive paper is graded based upon the size of grit that has been glued onto the backing paper. As shown in the table (left), the lower the number, the coarser the grit.

Grades of abrasive paper							
Grade	**Fine**			**Medium**		**Coarse**	
Grit size	220	180	150	120	100	80	60	40
Main use	Final step before finishing and sanding down between coats of finish.			Preparing for finishing.		Fast removal of rough material and imperfections.	

DON'T FORGET

The individual sheets of glass/garnet paper are normally marked on the reverse with the grit size (e.g. 220) and/or with the grade (e.g. fine).

Working through the Grades

When sanding wood with an abrasive paper, it is important to start with the most suitable grade of abrasive. This will depend on the amount of imperfections to be removed, although it's normally a fairly coarse grade, such as 60 or 80 grit. Next, systematically work through the grades until the surface is smooth and flat. Sanding with progressively finer grits removes the scratches left by the previous one and will eventually leave a smooth finish.

Sanding with the Grain

For the best results when sanding flat surfaces, you should wrap the abrasive paper round a sanding block and sand with the grain. The sanding block should be held flat on the surface, and with an even, steady pressure being applied, it should be worked back and forth along the grain. Any movement across the grain of the wood can leave deep scratches on the surface of the wood which can be difficult to remove.

Abrasive paper wrapped round a sanding block to be moved back and forth in the direction of the grain

DON'T FORGET

It's good practice to dampen the surface of the wood with a wet paper towel to raise the grain of the wood prior to using the fine grade abrasive paper.

THINGS TO DO AND THINK ABOUT

1. Prior to any finish being applied to wood, the surface must be properly prepared. State three stages in the preparation of the wooden surface before applying a finish.
2. State the purpose of a scraper.
3. Describe how to apply wood filler to repair a deep hole in a piece of wood.
4. State the two types of abrasive paper commonly used in woodworking.
5. Abrasive paper is available in a range of grades. State the name of the three main grades and the use for each grade.

ONLINE TEST

Test yourself on this topic on the Digital Zone.

APPLICATION AND TYPES OF SURFACE FINISH

VIDEO LINK

For additional videos on different finishing techniques, head to www.brightredbooks.net

DON'T FORGET

Paint should not be applied to your course work as it will obscure your project. If a colour effect is desired, a stain finish should be used instead.

FINISHING TECHNIQUES

Surface finishes are applied to wooden products for two main reasons, to protect the wood and to enhance the appearance of the wood. There are many finishes available and it's important that the correct finish is selected. When deciding on a suitable finish for a product, consideration must be given to the following factors:

- What level of protection is needed? Moisture, dirt, heat, sun, knocks and/or scratches?
- Safety – Is the finish child-friendly?
- Where will the product be used? Interior and/or exterior?
- What is the expected lifespan of the product?
- Must the grain be seen?
- Surface sheen required – high or low gloss.
- Drying time of applied finish.
- Ease of application and clean up.
- Number of coats required to achieve a quality finish.

TYPES OF SURFACE FINISH

Stain

A picture frame with a stain applied

Stain is used to change the colour of wood while allowing the grain still to be seen. Most stain finishes are not water-resistant and will require a further finish such as varnish that will seal and protect the wood from moisture. Stain can be applied using either a brush or a cloth. Stain can be used to make a cheap wood look like one which is more expensive or harder to obtain.

A selection of the numerous different shades and colours of stain that are available is shown

Oil

Oil finishes such as danish oil, linseed oil and olive (vegetable) oil are quick and easy to apply with either a brush or a cloth and provide a natural looking finish that enhances the grain of the wood. Although the three types of oil finish are suitable for both interior and exterior use, danish oil provides the most durable finish and is the best choice. Olive oil is colourless and has no odour, and for that reason, is frequently used on wooden products that come into contact with food. To maintain a protective coating, an oil finish will require regular reapplication around every six months.

An oil finish has endless applications including food preparation surfaces, sports equipment such as cricket bats, kitchen utensils, garden furniture, musical instruments, children's toys, wooden doors and wood turning projects.

DON'T FORGET

The terms Gloss, Silk and Matt refer to the sheen a surface finish will create. A gloss finish is a shiny smooth surface; silk, also known as a satin finish, is a slightly dull shiny surface; and a matt finish will leave a dull surface.

Garden furniture

Linseed oil

Wooden toys

Fruit bowl with an oil finish

Kitchen utensils

contd

Wax

A wax finish is used to achieve a smooth, silky, protective surface on a wooden workpiece. It produces a matt finish which allows the natural grain structure of the wood to be seen. Although applying wax directly onto bare wood will provide a light protective layer to the wood, to create an extra protective barrier to a workpiece, it is recommended that the wood is initially sealed with sanding sealer before being waxed. The purpose of applying the sanding sealer is to seal the pores of the wood to give a smooth, even surface for the top coats of wax.

Wax is a very easy finish to apply. Using steel wool, a thin coat of wax is rubbed into the wood in a circular motion, before being left to dry for around 30 minutes. Once dry, the surface of the wood can then be polished using a soft cloth. Just like an oil finish, to maintain a protective coating, a wax finish will require regular reapplication around every six months.

Steel wool

Wax being applied using steel wool

Varnish

Varnish produces a hard-wearing, durable, clear protective finish to wood that will be used either internally or externally. It is well suited to high-wear areas such as dining tables, floors and skirting boards due to the high level of protection it offers from stains, scruffs and scratches. Varnish is applied using a brush or cloth. To achieve a high-quality finish, it is recommended that at least three coats of varnish are applied, and between each coat, once it's fully dried, the surface should be lightly rubbed down with either a fine abrasive paper or steel wool. Once complete, a varnished surface will last for years and require very little maintenance.

Wax being polished using a soft cloth

A wooden surface, with a varnish finish applied to make it more durable

Interior varnish

Interior varnish being applied to a stair banister

DON'T FORGET

You need to protect your exterior wood from the weather. If you don't, it'll turn a grey/silvery colour in the sun and rot in the rain.

Exterior varnish   Exterior varnish being applied to an external table

External wooden windows and doors with varnish applied

THINGS TO DO AND THINK ABOUT

1. State five factors that should be considered when choosing which finish to apply to a workpiece.

2. State which surface finish should be selected to alter the colour of the wood, while allowing the grain of the wood still to be seen.

3. State which surface finish should be selected for a wooden kitchen utensil which will come into contact with food.

4. Describe the terms gloss, silk and matt finishes.

5. Explain why a varnished finish is suitable for dining tables, floors or skirting boards.

ONLINE TEST

Test yourself on types of finish at www.brightredbooks.net

CARE AND USE OF TOOLS AND SAFE AN SUSTAINABLE WORKING PRACTICES

SAFE WORKING PRACTICES

SAFETY IN THE WORKSHOP

While working in a workshop environment, it is extremely important that everyone acts with health and safety in mind. Carelessness and misbehaviour can very quickly and easily cause an accident to happen which could ultimately result in someone being injured or equipment being damaged. Due to the many potential dangers in a workshop, it is important that the following simple rules are followed:

- Always wear the appropriate personal protective equipment, for example, goggles, gloves, an apron, etc., for the activity you are undertaking.
- Remove, tuck in or tie any loose items including hair, tie and jewellery.
- Never run or fool around in the workshop and remember to carry tools safely.
- Keep the workshop tidy and free from any tripping hazards.
- Keep hands away from moving parts and, when using a chisel, you should always keep both hands behind the cutting edge.
- Only use equipment and machinery if you have received training and have permission to use it.
- Report all accidents, breakages and faults to your teacher, no matter how minor.
- Only use tools for their intended purpose.
- Never leave a machine unattended while the machine is running.
- Ensure that any guards fitted to machines are in good condition and are in place prior to using machinery.
- Ensure any work that is to be machined is secured in place prior to turning the power on.
- Know how to switch the power off to machines and where the emergency stop buttons are located throughout the workshop.

Learn where the emergency stop buttons are located around the workshop

DON'T FORGET

When you see this safety sign being displayed beside a machine, you'll need to check that the guard is in good condition and in place prior to turning the power to the machine on.

Guards must be used at all times

PERSONAL PROTECTIVE EQUIPMENT

The personal protective equipment (PPE) that you are required to wear will depend on what machine you are using and the task you are undertaking. Safety signs to show the PPE requirements for each machine will be displayed beside that machine. Examples of the various PPE available and the safety signs used are shown below.

ONLINE

Learn more about eye protection by reading the guide at www.brightredbooks.net

Wear face guard **Eye protection must be worn** **Protective apron must be worn** **Safety gloves must be worn** **Wear face mask**

Eye Protection

Special care should be taken to protect your eyes while operating machinery. The three main types of eye protection available are safety spectacles, safety goggles and the full-face visor.

Safety spectacles are suitable for the majority of eye protection needs you will be faced with while in the workshop. The wrap-around frames and impact-resistance safety lenses will provide adequate protection from medium-to-high impact flying objects.

Safety goggles provide complete eye protection. The main advantages safety goggles have over safety spectacles is that they:

Safety spectacles

contd

- offer protection from impacts from flying objects
- offer protection from elements in the air such as dust particles and debris, as well as liquid/chemical splashes
- are held securely against your face by an adjustable strap
- can be worn over existing prescription glasses.

Safety goggles

Protection from Dust

Wood dust can be inhaled and cause respiratory problems. With that in mind, whenever you are using a fixed machine or a portal power tool that creates wood dust, the dust extraction system attached to that machine should be activated. When no dust extraction system is in place, a dust protection mask should be used.

A dust extraction system in place on a wood lathe

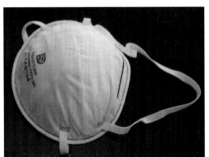

Dust protection mask

Visor and dust protection mask being worn while working on a wood lathe. The visor offers full face protection and is mainly recommended for use when working on a wood lathe

Protection for your Hands

There are a large variety of protective gloves available and care should be taken to select the correct type of glove for the task that is being undertaken. Your teacher or school technician may use protective gloves to offer enhanced grip while operating the circular saw or the planer to prepare the wood for your woodwork projects.

The most likely occasion you will need to wear gloves in the workshop is to protect your hands while applying a finish to your workpiece.

Safety gloves being worn to provide enhanced grip while using the band saw

REPORTING FAULTS AND FAULT-REPORTING SYSTEMS

Using a faulty tool, machine or power tool can be dangerous, and if you continue to use it while it's not working correctly, you can either cause further damage to the piece of equipment, or you could cause yourself or others an injury. With that in mind, it is important that you get into the habit of checking that all pieces of equipment are in good working order before and after use. This is something you will be expected to show evidence of when completing your log book for the practical activity section of the course assessment. If you do notice a fault with a piece of equipment, this should be reported to your teacher, who will arrange for it to be either repaired or replaced.

Disposable gloves can be used while applying a wood finish then discarded after use

It is recommended to wear an apron while working in a workshop. Not only will it protect your clothes from dust, it will help hold loose clothing in place

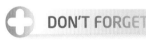 **DON'T FORGET**

Due to the increased risk of entanglement, protective gloves should not be worn while using rotating machinery such as pillar drills and lathes.

THINGS TO DO AND THINK ABOUT

1. State six safety rules that should be observed while working in a workshop.
2. Draw a plan of the workshop you work in and highlight on it the location of the emergency stop buttons that have been installed around the room.
3. Describe two main differences between safety spectacles and safety goggles.
4. State a reason for a dust extraction system being fitted on a machine.
5. State a reason for wearing an apron while working in a workshop.

ONLINE TEST

Test yourself on safe working practices on the Digital Zone.

SUSTAINABILITY AND RECYCLING

SUSTAINABILITY

DON'T FORGET

When you see the FSC trademark on a piece of wood, it certifies that the wood supplier is committed to providing wood that has come from a sustainable, managed forest. For more information, visit www.fsc-uk.org

Before any product is made, there is a responsibility on behalf of the designer to consider the sustainability of the product. Sustainability refers to the need to ensure that the materials and energy we use today are going to be available for a long time into the future. In terms of practical woodworking, consideration should be given to the following sustainability concepts:

- sourcing and cost of materials
- waste and cutting allowances
- recycling and reusing materials

Sourcing and cost of material

Unlike most of the materials we consume such as metal and plastic, wood is a renewable material. It's easiest to think of renewable materials as things that can grow, so if you're thinking of renewables, ask if you can grow this item. Softwood is known as being one of the most efficient renewable materials available since it's fast growing and can be renewed within a few years. When sourcing wood for a project, it is good practice to source wood that has come from a managed forest. The term managed forest means that for every tree cut down, a new tree will be planted to replace it. The Forestry Stewardship Council (FSC) is an international organisation that promotes the sustainable management of forests, and certifies that products such as wood, paper and card that carry the FSC logo are produced from trees that come from responsibly managed forests.

A new tree being planted to ensure the future supply of wood

As well as sourcing wood that is from a managed forest, you should be prepared to consider alternatives that have less of a strain on the environment, and which will ultimately provide a more sustainable product. For instance, selecting a cheaper, faster growing softwood rather than a more expensive, harder to obtain, hardwood. Another consideration that could be adopted is to use a manufactured board, such as veneered MDF, over natural timber. Veneered MDF offers the look of a natural timber while being a cheaper and more environmentally friendly alternative that is made from recycled materials such as small wood particles and saw dust.

Waste and Cutting Allowances

There are a few techniques that can be adopted in a woodworking workshop that can help with achieving the most efficient use of the materials available and produce minimum waste, for instance:

DON'T FORGET

Some tropical hardwoods are becoming scarce and further use of them will deplete them further.

VIDEO LINK

Find out more about sustainable forests by watching the clip on the Digital Zone.

DON'T FORGET

When calculating how many strips of wood can be cut from an individual board, remember that the wastage produced by each saw cut should be factored in.

- When marking out parts that are to be cut out of sheet material, the position of the cuts should be marked out in the corner of the sheet rather than in the middle of the sheet. This will not only reduce waste, it will make cutting out the shape easier.

- When several parts of the same shape are required, a template can be used to help with marking out.

- Being aware of the standard sizes of wood that are available, then selecting the size that is nearest to what is required will reduce the amount that is required to be machined down to size.

A template being used

- Similarly, when the width of component parts for a project is being decided, a calculation should be made to work out how many strips of wood can be cut from the overall width of the available board. It might be the case that if the width of the strips were reduced slightly, and the reduction in width won't have an impact on the function of the part, an extra strip of wood can be cut out of the board. If that's the case, then this should be considered as this would be the most efficient use of the material and help improve the sustainability of the product.

contd

- Another important factor to help reduce wastage in the workshop is repairing broken pieces of projects rather than just replacing them with new pieces of materials. For example, the next time you are making a project and a piece of wood breaks off, try gluing it back together rather than just scrapping it and starting over again with a new piece of wood.

- The same can be said for tools and machines, and one way of increasing a piece of equipment's shelf-life is by regular maintenance. If we choose not to maintain our tools/machines by oiling the parts, sharpening the blades or replacing some of the consumable parts of the product efficiently, then we are lowering its sustainability as an item.

RECYCLING

Recycling and Reusing Materials

The term recycling a material means that at the end of the material's life, it is broken down then processed into a new, usable product.

Some examples of recycled wooden products that have been reprocessed into a range of wood-based materials are animal bedding and landscaping products, as shown above

Bark chippings used for garden landscaping

Before binning an old wooden product, consider what you can reuse that wood for. One simple reuse of a product can increase sustainability

The term **reuse** is often confused with **recycle**, but the main difference with reuse is that you're not breaking the product down: what you are effectively doing is taking an item and using it again, but perhaps for a different purpose.

Making products from old pallet wood is becoming increasingly popular and is a good example of reusing material for a different purpose to increase the lifespan of the material and increase sustainability

VIDEO LINK

Learn about wood recycling by watching the clip at www.brightredbooks.net

THINGS TO DO AND THINK ABOUT

In your own words, explain the following sustainability concepts:

- sourcing and cost of materials
- waste and cutting allowances
- recycling and reusing materials.

ONLINE TEST

Test your knowledge of this concept on the Digital Zone.

COURSE ASSESSMENT

COURSE ASSESSMENT STRUCTURE

The course assessment comprises two components, the practical activity and the question paper. The practical activity will involve manufacturing a project set by SQA while completing a log book, and the question paper will be set by SQA and will be one hour in duration. Between these two instruments of assessment, SQA will provide you with the opportunity to demonstrate and provide evidence of your skills, knowledge and understanding of a variety of the various concepts listed in their course assessment specification. The marks achieved from the practical activity and question paper are combined, and then the total mark will determine the final grade awarded. The course assessment is graded A–D.

QUESTION PAPER BRIEF

The purpose of the question paper is to sample and evidence those areas of the course assessment which cannot be evidenced through the practical activity and the log book.

The question paper consists of several scenario-based questions with a spread of marks covering the topic areas listed on the right.

The question paper has 60 marks out of a total of 130 marks. This is scaled by SQA to represent 30% of the overall marks for the course assessment.

Topic area	Range of marks
Measuring and marking out tools	4–6
Reading and interpreting drawings	4–6
Materials	4–6
Benchwork	5–7
Flat-frame construction and assembly	6–8
Carcase construction and assembly	6–8
Use and care of machines and power tools	8–10
Surface preparation	5–8
Health and safety	6–8
Sustainability and recycling	3–5

Command Words

Make sure you read each question thoroughly so you understand exactly what is being asked. Remember to answer questions correctly if you are asked to:

- **State**: Use the correct terminology to name or state what is being asked for.
- **Describe**: Give a descriptive account or details of processes, steps, properties and so on.
- **Explain**: Describe your answer, but this time with justification and reasons. Think about how and why.

Examples of each type of question using the command words **state**, **describe** and **explain** are given below:

1. The handle was manufactured from a wooden blank on a wood lathe. **Describe** the four stages in preparing a wooden blank prior to fitting it to the lathe. (4)
2. The blank was turned to a cylinder. **State** the name of a turning tool used to produce the cylinder. (1)
3. The handle is manufactured from a softwood rather than a hardwood. **Explain** why the use of a softwood is considered more environmentally friendly than the use of a hardwood. (1)

Question Paper Practice

One of the best forms of revision is to practise answering exam type questions. This will allow you to see the level of knowledge and understanding that is required and become familiar with the structure of the question paper you will be sitting in the actual exam. The specimen paper on the National 5 Practical Woodworking section of the SQA website is an ideal starting point. The specimen paper includes marking instructions which will also help you to understand the standard that SQA are looking for in your answers.

PRACTICAL ACTIVITY

The six sections that make up the practical activity and the total amount of marks allocated to each section are shown.

The practical activity has 70 marks out of a total 130 marks. This is scaled by SQA to represent 70% of the overall marks for the course assessment.

Section	Total marks allocated
Log book	15
Flat-frame construction	12
Carcase construction	12
Machining and turnery	11
Finishing	10
Overall assembly	10

Understanding the Standard

The standards and tolerances that your artefact will be assessed against are shown.

As you work through the practical activity, it is important that you understand what you are being assessed on and what the required standard is. The pictures shown below should help exemplify these standards.

Operation	Tolerance
Planing (or similar)	± 1mm
Marking out and cutting	± 1mm
Machine/power tools tasks: • Vertical drilling • Sanding to a line • Drilling to given line position	± 1mm
Joint gaps	Not to exceed 1mm
Overall sizes	± 3mm

This joint has been marked out accurately and has met the standard of tolerance required

Your joints should be marked out using the correct tools and equipment to within the required tolerance of ± 1mm

This hole has not met the standard of specified tolerance required as it has been drilled off-centre

It is important to drill accurately. Not only do you need to drill in the correct position, you need to drill to the specified depth

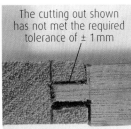
The cutting out shown has not met the required tolerance of ± 1mm

When cutting out care should be taken to accurately cut out all joints to the specified tolerance of ± 1mm

Remember to remove any scratches left from using abrasives

When sanding to a line, you are required to sand to a tolerance of ± 1mm

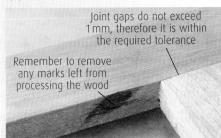
Joint gaps do not exceed 1mm, therefore it is within the required tolerance

Remember to remove any marks left from processing the wood

Square shoulders

Your turnery should be symmetrical with a smooth finish and have good square shoulders where required. The final dimensions of the turnery should meet the dimensions specified in the working drawing within the practical activity assessment task

Your assembled frame should be square and free of twists

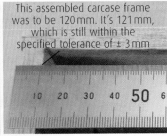
This assembled carcase frame was to be 120mm. It's 121mm, which is still within the specified tolerance of ± 3mm

The overall size of an assembly should be checked to make sure it is within the specified tolerance of ± 3mm

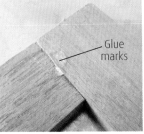
Glue marks

Prior to applying a finish, all pencil marks and glue marks should be removed

Accumulation of excess varnish

When applying a finish, care should be taken to avoid any obvious blemishes such as visible runs or accumulation of excess varnish or oil

THINGS TO DO AND THINK ABOUT

Download the National 5 Practical Woodworking Specimen Paper from the SQA website then try to complete it within the time allocated. Once complete, check your answers using the marking instructions provided to see how well you've done!

PRACTICAL ACTIVITIES

LOG BOOK

While working on the manufacture of the artefact section of the practical activity, you will be required to complete a log book. The mandatory log book, which is issued by SQA, carries a weighting of 15 marks of the 70 marks allocated to the practical activity. The three areas that are assessed within the log book are listed below, with each area being worth five marks in total:

- Machine and power tool care and maintenance
- Tool care and maintenance
- Safe working procedures

Machine and Power Tool Care Maintenance

For the machine and power tool care and maintenance section, you are expected to accurately record five occasions when you set up a machine or prepared a power tool for safe use. Within each description, you should ensure you have indicated the checks you made to the machine or power tool both prior to and after using that piece of equipment. If you have had to undertake any remedial action to repair or rectify a fault then this should be included in your description of the checks you have carried out. You are free to select any five to record in your log book. Examples of procedural checks to undertake are given below:

- Setting up a woodturning lathe, belt sander, disc sander, pillar/pedestal drill or mortise machine.
- Preparing a cordless or corded drill, cordless screwdriver, orbital sander, belt sander or a jig saw.

Some common procedural checks to undertake **prior to using** a machine or power tool are listed below:

- You have been shown how and have been given permission by your teacher to use the machine or power tool.
- You have familiarised yourself with the location of any emergency stop buttons that are fitted to the machine.
- The workpiece is secured.
- The guard, if fitted, is in place.
- The dust extraction, if fitted, is in place.
- The table, if fitted, is secured in place and set at the correct angle and height for the procedure to be carried out.
- All parts, for example, sanding belts, drill bits, saw blades, plugs, cables and guards are in good working order and securely fitted.

Before using a machine, you should familiarise yourself with the location of any emergency stops that are fitted to that machine. An emergency foot stop that is fitted to a pillar/pedestal drill is shown above

contd

Some common procedural checks to undertake **after using** a machine or power tool are listed below:

- The machine's power is switched off and the isolator is turned to the off position.
- The power tool is switched off and if it's corded, it is unplugged, and the cord is checked for damage.
- If the power tool is cordless, check the remaining battery life left and consider putting it on charge ready for its next use.
- Remove the drill bit/screwdriver bit from the chuck and store it away.
- Remove the chuck key, if used with that machine/power tool.
- Clear any waste wood/sawdust left on the machine after use.
- If the tool rest on the wood lathe has been moved out of the way for sanding purposes, reposition it to its centred position on the bed of the lathe.
- Report any faults of, or damage to, the machines or power tools to your teacher to arrange for them to be repaired/replaced.

Tool Care and Maintenance

This section of the log book requires you to describe the procedures you undertook to set up, adjust or repair up to five different tools during the manufacture of your course assessment artefact. Your description should outline any remedial action you took to fix/adjust/repair the tool, followed by the steps you carried out to check the tool was in good working order. A selection of scenarios you could undertake and record in your log book are given below:

- Replacing a broken coping saw blade.
- Setting a rebate plane to cut a rebate to a set depth and width.
- Setting a plough plane to cut a groove to a set depth and specific position.
- Setting a hand router to cut to a set depth.
- Setting a marking gauge to mark a line parallel to an edge to a specific depth.
- Honing a cutting edge on a chisel.
- Honing a cutting edge on a plane iron.

Safe Working Procedures

The mark you receive for safe working procedures will be solely based on whether you have acted with health and safety in mind throughout the manufacture of your course assessment artefact. Your teacher will be observing your behaviour within the workshop and will be keeping a record of any reminders about inappropriate or unsafe behaviour they have had to issue to you. They will also record any interventions they have had to make to prevent unsafe use of any tools, machines or power tools. If you adhere to safe working procedures and your teacher has not had to issue you with any reminders or make any interventions then you will receive the full five marks allocated to this section of the practical activity.

DON'T FORGET

One of the procedures SQA insist that you undertake and record in your log book is either honing a cutting edge on a chisel or a plane iron.

Sharpening equipment

THINGS TO DO AND THINK ABOUT

It is important to reinforce the skills, knowledge and understanding you have gained while working through the course in some way. A good technique is to produce a mind map. Why not try producing a mind map to summarise what you have learned from each chapter in this book?

An example of a mind map based on the wood lathe

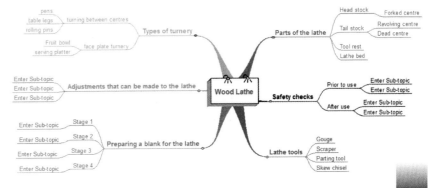

QUESTIONS

QUESTIONS 1

QUESTIONS

1 The frame for a coffee table is shown. The designer wanted to create a contrast in the design by making the legs from a light-coloured softwood and the rails from a dark-coloured hardwood.

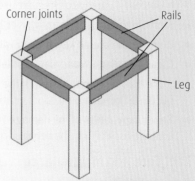

   (a) Name a suitable softwood for the legs. (1)

   (b) Name a suitable hardwood for the rails. (1)

   (c) A selection of possible joints that could be used to join the rails to the leg are shown below. State the name of each joint shown. (3)

Joint A 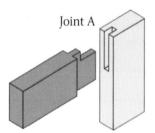   Joint B 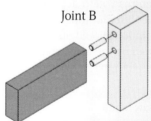   Joint C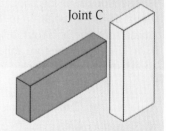

   (d) In the end, the designer chose to join the rails to the leg using Joint A. State a reason for choosing Joint A over the other possible joints. (1)

2 A joiner was asked by her local primary school to make a stand for their natural Christmas tree. She came up with the stand below.

   An exploded view of the joint she used to construct the stand is shown below.

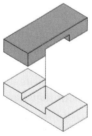

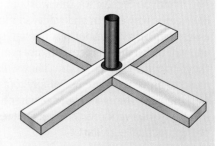

   (a) State the name of this joint. (1)

   (b) State the name of a suitable adhesive used in the assembly of the stand. (1)

3 Two different picture frames, Frame A and Frame B, have been made and are shown below. State the name of the joint used in each frame. (2)

Frame A   Frame B

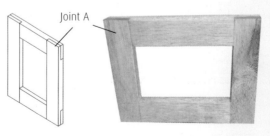

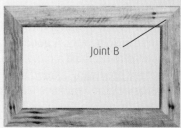

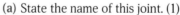

contd

4   A scissor holder is shown below.

   (a) A drill bit was used to drill the
large holes required to store the
scissors. State the name of a
suitable **drill bit**. (1)

   (b) State the name of the **machine** used
to drill the large holes. (1)

   (c) Describe a technique to use to
prevent the wood from splitting
while drilling the hole all the way
through. (1)

large diameter
hole drilled

Through
housing joint

5   Several tools were used in the manufacture of the scissors holder.
State which **three** hand tools the following terms are associated with:

   (a) Stem, stock, spur, thumb screw (1)

   (b) Blade, tang, ferrule, handle (1)

   (c) Cap iron, cutting iron, adjusting leaver, adjusting nut (1)

6   A calendar is shown below.

The joints used in the manufacture of the calendar are highlighted in the
pictures below.

   (a) State the name of joint A. (1)   (b) State the name of joint B. (1)

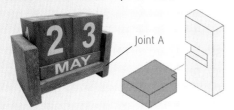

Joint A

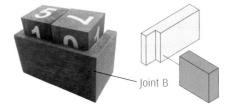

Joint B

7   The candle holder shown below was created on a wood lathe.

A picture of part of the wood lathe is shown below.

Part A

Part B

Part C

Curved
shape

   (a) State the name of the part of the wood lathe labelled **Part A**. (1)

   (b) Explain the purpose of adjusting **Part B**. (1)

   (c) Explain the purpose of adjusting **Part C**. (1)

   (d) State the name of the lathe tool used to create the curved shape on the
candle holder. (1)

   (e) The candle holder had a clear varnish finished applied to it.
State a reason for applying a finish to the candle holder. (1)

QUESTIONS 2

QUESTIONS

A child's nursery chair is shown below.

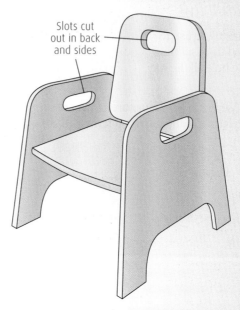

Slots cut out in back and sides

1 The chair is made from plywood. State two reasons for this choice of material. (2)

2 State the name of another suitable manufactured board that could have been used instead of plywood. (1)

3 Describe the main differences in the construction between plywood and the manufactured board you named in question 2. Sketches may be used to help illustrate your answer. (2)

4 A template was used to mark out the shape of the sides. State two reasons for using a template. (2)

5 State the name of a **portable power tool** that could be used to cut out the shape of the sides of the chair. (1)

6 Describe two safety precautions that should be observed while using a power tool. (2)

7 To help with lifting the chair, a **slot** was cut out of the sides and back. Describe how the hand tool shown could be used to cut the slots in the chair. You should state the name of the hand tool shown in your answer. (2)

contd

8 The chair was assembled using the fixing shown below.
   State the name of this type of fixing. (1)

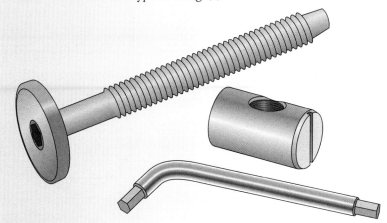

9 Explain a benefit of using this type of fixing over a traditional method of joining. (1)

10 The drill bit used to create the holes required for the fixing is shown below. State the
   name of the drill bit. (1)

11 The drill bit could have been used to create the holes by using any of the following
   pieces of equipment. State the name of each one. (3)

Machine A: Power tool B: Hand tool C:

12 State a safety check that should be carried out before starting Machine A. (1)

13 The chair has a varnish finish applied. State two reasons for applying a finish to the
   chair. (2)

14 Before the varnish was applied, the surfaces were rubbed down with an abrasive
   paper. State the name of two types of abrasive paper. (2)

15 Abrasive paper is available in three main grades. Coarse is one of the grades, state the
   name of the other two. (2)

QUESTIONS 3

QUESTIONS

An outdoor sand pit for a children's nursery is shown below.

1 State the name of a suitable softwood used for the sand pit. (1)

2 The nursery wanted the sand pit to be finished in a variety of primary colours but still wanted to be able to see the natural grain of the wood. State the name of a suitable finish. (1)

3 The sand pit was made by basic joinery techniques. Identify each tool and power tool used in the construction of the sandpit. (10)

Tool A: Tool B: Tool C:

Tool D: Tool E: Tool F: Tool G: Power tool H:

Enlarged view of tip

Enlarged view of tip

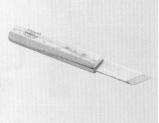

contd

Power tool I: Power tool J:

4   Describe safety precautions to observe while using power tools H, I and J. (3)

5   The sides of the sand pit were attached to the legs using countersink screws. The three holes, A, B and C were drilled in preparation for fixing the side to the leg. State the name of hole A, hole B and hole C. (3)

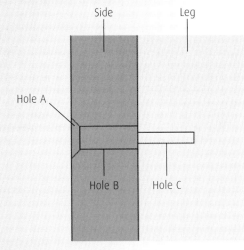

6   State a reason why a countersink screw was used. (1)

7   An alternative method of fixing the side to the leg could be to use a hammer and nails. State the full name of the hammer and nail shown below. (2)

Hammer: Nail:

QUESTIONS 4

QUESTIONS

1 A paper block holder is shown below.

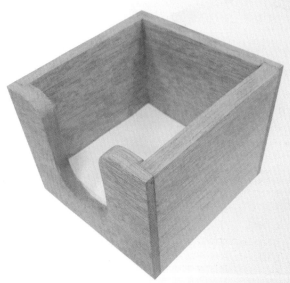

The wood joint shown was used in the manufacture of the paper block holder. State the name of this joint. (1)

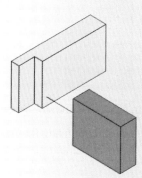

2 A butt joint was originally considered for joining the frame of the paper block holder. State a possible reason why this joint was rejected. (1)

3 The tool shown below was used in the manufacture of the paper block holder. State the name of this tool. (1)

4 Name the four parts of this tool labelled A, B, C and D. (4)

5 The holder frame was manufactured from a hardwood. State the name of a suitable hardwood. (1)

6 State a reason why softwood could be considered more environmentally friendly than hardwood. (1)

7 Describe how plywood is constructed to give it strength. You may use a sketch to illustrate your answer. (1)

contd

8 Plywood was chosen for the base. Other than its strength, state two reasons why plywood was chosen. (2)

9 A plough plane was used to cut a groove into the sides of the paper block holder to hold the plywood base in place.

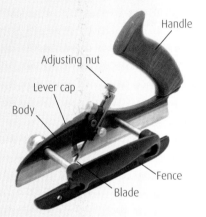

Groove

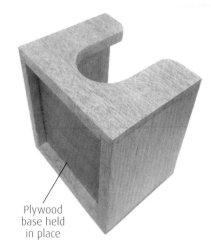

Plywood base held in place

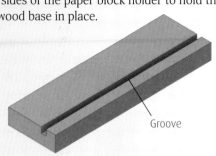

Handle
Adjusting nut
Lever cap
Body
Fence
Blade

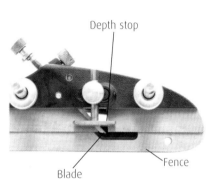

Depth stop
Blade
Fence

A plough plane is shown above   Depth stop and adjustable fence of a plough plane

The information below describes how the plough plane can be adjusted. Using the words listed below, fill in the blanks labelled A–C. (3)

Groove   Adjusting   Fence   Distance   Blade

The plough plane has a depth stop to determine the depth of cut made by the
_____A_____ and an adjustable _____B_____ which controls the distance the
_____C_____ is from the edge of the wood.

10 The tools shown below were used to drill the large hole required in the front of the paper block holder. State the name of these tools. (2)

Tool A: Tool B:

11 Describe a method of preventing the wood from splitting when boring the large hole. (1)

12 The frame of the paper block holder was assembled without glue and checked for squareness. State the name of this procedure. (1)

13 Other than sanding, state two stages in the preparation of the wood prior to applying a finish. (2)

14 A wax finish was applied. State two reasons for applying a finish. (2)

15 A working drawing for the paper block holder was produced. State two items of information a working drawing would show. (2)

QUESTIONS 5

QUESTIONS

A coffee table is shown below.

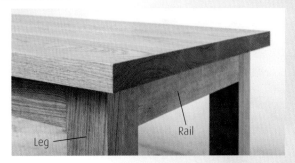

Haunched mortise and tenon joints were used to join the legs to the rails. The tool shown below was used to mark out the joints.

1 State the name of this tool. (1)

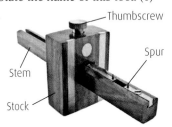

2 State two adjustments that can be made to this tool. (2)

3 The following chisels were used in the manufacture of the mortise and tenon joints. State the names of these chisels. (2)

Chisel A:

Chisel B:

4 Each chisel has a metal ring fitted tightly round the neck of their handle. State the name given to the metal ring fitted to the handle. (1)

5 State the purpose of the metal ring fitted to the handle. (1)

6 Describe a technique to use to ensure that the mortise in the leg is cut to the correct depth. (1)

7 State a safety precaution that should be observed when using a chisel. (1)

8 The following tools were used in the manufacture of the coffee table. State the name of these tools. (3)

Tool A: Tool B: Tool C:

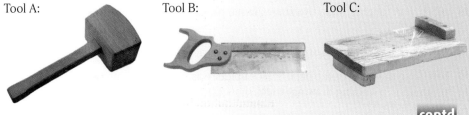

contd

9 While manufacturing a mortise and tenon joint, it is good practice to ensure your workpiece is held securely in place. The following holding devices could be used. State the name of each device. (2)

Device A Device B:

10 The table top is made up of strips of red pine glued together. State the name of a suitable glue. (1)

11 State the name of a holding device that can be used to hold the strips while the glue dries. (1)

12 State the name of a portable machine that can be used to smooth the top surface of the table. (1)

13 The table top has been chamfered.

State the name of the hand tool used to create the chamfer. (1)

14 The frame of the table was attached to the table top by using the screw and fixing shown below. State the names of the type of screw and fixing. (2)

Screw: Fixing:

15 The manufactured board shown on the right is commonly used for table tops. State the name of the manufactured board. (1)

16 The machine shown below could have been used in the manufacture of the coffee table. State the name of this machine. (1)

QUESTIONS 6

QUESTIONS

1 A child's stool is shown below.

The stool was made from mahogany. State the name of another hardwood which could be used. (1)

2 The corners of the stool top have been rounded to remove the sharp edges. State the name of the **machine** that could be used to round the corners. (1)

3 A forstner bit was used to drill the large diameter holes in the stool sides. State the name of another drill bit that could be used. (1)

4 Describe a method of preventing the wood from splitting when drilling the hole. (1)

5 The stool sides were attached to the stool top by using the mechanical fixings shown. State the name given to this type of mechanical fixing. (1)

6 A wood lathe, shown below, was used to produce the decorative turned rail of the child's stool.
State the names of **Part A, Part B, Part C** and **Part D**. (4)

7 When turning between centres, a forked centre is used. State the purpose of a forked centre. (1)

contd

8 When turning between centres, either a revolving (live) centre or a dead centre can be used. State an advantage of using a revolving centre rather than a dead centre. (1)

Dead Centre

9 The turned rail was manufactured from a wooden blank on the wood lathe. The first stage of preparing the blank for the lathe is shown below. Describe the remaining three main stages in preparing a wooden blank to be turned on a wood lathe. (3)

Stage 1

Using a steel rule, mark diagonals on both ends to locate the centre.

10 The turned rail was initially turned down to a cylinder of Ø 40 mm. State the name of the tool used to check the diameter of the wooden blank while it was still on the wood lathe. (1)

11 State the name of the lathe tool used to turn the wooden blank down to a cylinder. (1)

12 State the name of the lathe tool used to make the shape at A. (1)

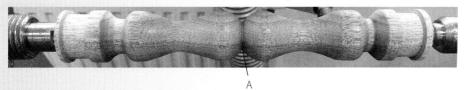

A

13 As you can see from the picture below, lathe tools come with long handles. State two reasons for the long handles. (2)

Parting chisel

14 The rail was sanded prior to removing it from the lathe. State two adjustments that should be carried out before sanding. (2)

QUESTIONS 7

QUESTIONS

1 A tea tray is shown below.

Tray base

Concave curve

Tray side

Tray handle

The tray handles and sides are manufactured from Meranti, which is a hardwood. Describe two **environmental** reasons for choosing to use a softwood instead of a hardwood. (2)

2 The tray base is made from plywood. State two reasons for this choice of material. (2)

3 **(a)** The handles were turned between centres using a wood lathe. One of the handles is shown below. The finished length of each handle is 270 mm. State a reason for using a blank that is 300 mm long to turn each handle. (1)

(b) State the purpose of the **tailstock** on the wood lathe. (1)

Square shoulder   Rounded corner

Two lathe tools used in the manufacture of the handles are shown below.

(c) State the name of the turning tool used to produce the square shoulders. (1)

(d) State the name of the turning tool used to produce the rounded corners. (1)

4 The handle was sanded while it was still on the lathe. State an adjustment that could be made to the wood lathe to improve the surface finish of the handle. (1)

5 The marking out aid shown below was used when marking out the outline of the tray sides.

(a) State the name given to such a marking out aid. (1)

(b) State a reason for its use. (1)

6 The tool shown below was used to create the concave (internal) curve on the sides of the tray. State the name of this tool. (1)

contd

7 (a) A drill bit was used to create the large flat-bottomed hole in the sides of the tray. State the name of a suitable drill bit. (1)

   (b) A drill bit was used to create the screw holes in the sides of the tray. State the name of a suitable drill bit. (1)

   (c) State the name of the **machine** that the drill bits are used with. (1)

   (d) State one safety precaution that should be observed **before** drilling. (1)

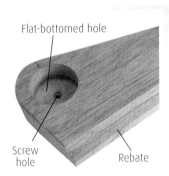

Flat-bottomed hole

Screw hole

Rebate

8 A rebate plane was used to create the rebate to accommodate the plywood base. The plywood was attached using adhesive and nails. The nails used are shown on the right.

   (a) State the name of this type of nail. (1)

   (b) The tools shown below were used while attaching the plywood base. State the name of Tool A and Tool B. (2)

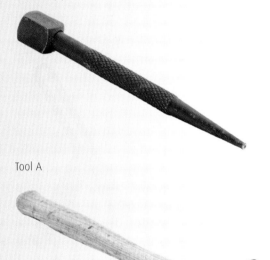

Tool A

Tool B

   (c) State the purpose of Tool A. (1)

   (d) While hammering one of the nails in place, the nail bent and required to be removed. The tool used to remove the nail is shown. State the name of the tool used. (1)

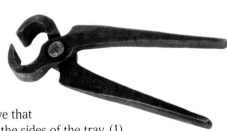

   (e) State the name of a suitable adhesive that could be used to attach the base to the sides of the tray. (1)

9 State the name of an abrasive paper suitable for removing pencil marks from the wood. (1)

10 A finish was applied to the tea tray. State **two** reasons for applying a finish. (2)

QUESTIONS

1 A shoe rack is shown below.

The joint shown below was used to join the shelves to the sides.

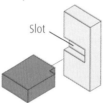

State the name of this joint. (1)

2 The tool shown was used when marking out the sloping angles of the slots on the sides of the shoe rack.

State the name of the tool shown. (1)

3 The chisel shown below was used during the manufacture of the shoe rack. The main parts of the chisel are labelled.

(a) State the name of Part A. (1)   **(b)** State the name of Part B. (1)   **(c)** State the name of Part C. (1)   **(d)** State the full name of this chisel. (1)

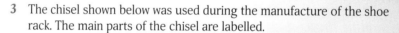
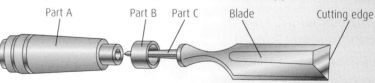

Parts of a chisel

4 **(a)** The tool shown was used to level off the bottom of the slot in the sides of the shoe rack.

   State the name of this tool. (1)

   (b) With reference to the picture of the tool shown, describe how you would set this tool to finish the joint to a depth of 9 mm. (2)

contd

5 (a) The holding device shown below was used to hold the side securely in place while cutting out the joints. State the name of the holding device. (1)

   (b) When the holding device was tightened, it damaged the surface of the shoe rack side. Describe how this damage could have been avoided. (1)

6 A hand saw was used to cut out the curved corner on the sides. State the name of a suitable **hand saw**. (1)

7 The cutting list shown was found on the working drawing for the shoe rack.

   (a) The cutting list states the material to be used for the shoe rack is softwood. State the name of a suitable softwood. (1)

   (b) State **two other** items of information that would be included in a working drawing. (2)

Cutting List					
Project: Shoe Rack					
Part	**Number Required**	**Material**	**Dimensions**		
			Length	**Breadth**	**Thickness**
Side	2	Softwood	500	300	18
Shelf	2	Softwood	418	300	18
Stopper	2	Softwood	400	50	18

8 The stopper was attached to the bottom of the shelves to prevent the shoes from falling off. The stopper was attached using screws, the type of screw used is shown below.

   (a) State the name of this type of screw. (1)

   (b) State a reason why this type of screw was used. (1)

   (c) The screws were fixed in place using the screwdriver shown below. State the name of this type of screwdriver. (1)

   Enlarged view of the tip of the screwdriver.

   (d) Part of the process of attaching the stopper to the shelf involved using the tool shown below. State the name of this tool. (1)

   (e) State the purpose of this tool. (1)

9 (a) When the shoe rack was being assembled, it was dry clamped. Explain what is meant by the term **dry clamping**. (1)

   (b) The holding device shown was used to dry clamp the shoe rack. State the name of this holding device. (1)

   (c) Describe two adjustments that can be made to the holding device. (2)

10 (a) Other than sanding, state two stages in the preparation of the wood prior to applying a finish. (2)

   (b) A varnish finish was applied to the shoe rack. Describe a suitable method of applying the finish. (1)

QUESTIONS 9

QUESTIONS

1 A TV cabinet is shown.

(a) The TV cabinet is made from a manufactured board. State the name of a suitable manufactured board. (1)

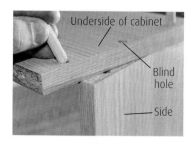

(b) The joint used to join the top of the TV cabinet to the sides is shown on the left.

State the name of the joint used. (1)

(c) A blind hole is a hole that is drilled to a specified depth without breaking through to the other side of the workpiece. A pillar drill was used when drilling the blind holes in the top and sides of the TV cabinet. Describe a method of ensuring the depth is 12 mm. (1)

2 A planter for bedding plants is shown on the left.

A stub mortise and tenon joint was used to join the legs to the rails and is shown below.

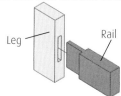

(a) State the names of **two** marking out tools which could be used to mark out a stub mortise and tenon joint. (2)

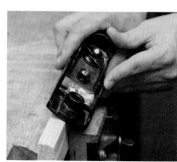

(b) When the planter was assembled, a **waterproof** adhesive was used. Explain why a waterproof adhesive was chosen. (1)

(c) The hand tool used to make the chamfers on the legs and rails of the planter is shown on the left.

State the full name of the hand tool. (1)

(d) The sides of the planter are made from a thin, multilayered manufactured board. State the name of a suitable manufacture board. (1)

3 A hexagonal wall shelf is shown.

(a) State the name of a suitable abrasive paper that could be used to smooth down the wall shelf prior to applying the finish. (1)

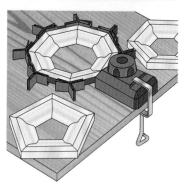

(b) The hexagonal shaped wall shelf was assembled using the holding device shown on the left.

State the name of this device. (1)

4 A candle holder manufactured from a used whisky barrel is shown below.

(a) State an **environmental** reason for reusing the wood from an old whisky barrel in the manufacture of the candle holder. (1)

contd

(b) The hardwood which the barrel is made from is a very strong, very durable, heavy and hard timber which responds well to steam-bending. It is golden brown in colour with a highly figured grain. State the name of a suitable hardwood. (1)

(c) Flat-bottomed holes were drilled into the wood to accommodate the candles.

Flat-bottomed hole

State the name of a suitable drill bit used to create the flat-bottomed holes in the candle holder. (1)

(d) A wax finish was applied to the candle holder. State **two** reasons for applying a finish. (2)

5   An extract from a working drawing for a picture frame is shown below.

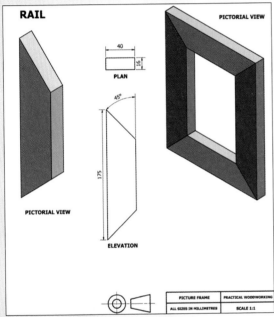

The cutting list for the component part featured in the working drawing is shown below.

Cutting list			Project: Picture frame		
Part	Number required	Material	Dimensions		
			Length	Breadth	Thickness
Answer A	Answer B	Any suitable softwood	Answer C	Answer D	Answer E

(a) Complete the cutting list using the information provided in the working drawing. (2)

(b) State the unit of measurement used in the working drawing. (1)

(c) State the name of a suitable softwood. (1)

(d) The holding device used to hold the picture frame together while the glue sets is shown below.

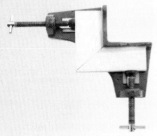

State the name of this device. (1)

QUESTIONS 10

QUESTIONS

1   A wood lathe with the main parts labelled is shown below.

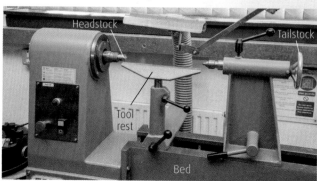

The wood lathe was used in the manufacture of the kitchen towel holder shown on the right.

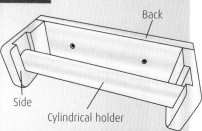

(a) A lathe operator turned the cylindrical roller on the wood lathe. An apron was worn for protection when working on the wood lathe. State the name of **two** other pieces of personal protective equipment that should be worn. (2)

(b) While the wooden blank is being turned on the wood lathe, it is held between two centres. State the name of the **two** centres. (2)

(c) The wooden blank was reduced to a cylinder using a gouge. Sketch the blade of this lathe tool. (1)

(d) The hand tool shown below was used in the preparation of the wooden blank for the lathe.

State the name of this tool. (1)

(e) State the purpose of the adjusting lever. (1)

(f) State the purpose of the adjusting nut. (1)

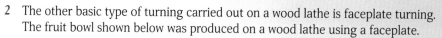

2   The other basic type of turning carried out on a wood lathe is faceplate turning. The fruit bowl shown below was produced on a wood lathe using a faceplate.

Part of the preparation for faceplate turning involves attaching a faceplate, shown above, onto a prepared wooden blank.

(a) The faceplate is attached to the wooden blank using wood screws. State the name of a suitable **power tool** that could be used to insert the screws into the wooden blank. (1)

(b) The faceplate is then mounted directly onto the wood lathe as shown below.

State the name of the part of the wood lathe the faceplate is secured onto. (1)

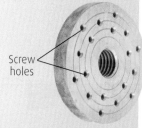

(c) The fruit bowl was sanded while the bowl was still attached to the wood lathe. Describe an adjustment that could be made to the wood lathe to improve the surface finish of the bowl. (1)

(d) Vegetable oil was applied to the fruit bowl. Explain why this type of finish is important. (1)

contd

3   A child's Christmas Eve box is shown on the right.

(a) Two types of joint used in the manufacture of the box are shown below.

Plywood lid

Lid frame

Box carcass

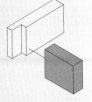

Joint A

Joint B

(i) State the name of joint A. (1)

(ii) State the name of joint B. (1)

(b) The tool shown below was used in the marking out of Joint A.

Thumbscrew

Stem

Spur   Stock

State the name of this tool. (1)

(c) Describe how this tool can be set to 8mm using a steel rule. (2)

(d) The carcase of the box had a groove cut into the sides to accommodate a hardboard base and the lid frame had a rebate cut into the top of it to accommodate the plywood lid.

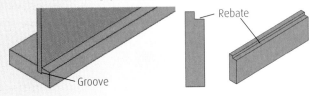

Rebate

Groove

State the name of the tool which can cut out both a groove and a rebate in wood. (1)

4   A mirror frame is shown on the right.

(a) A selection of possible joints for the mirror frame are shown below.

Joint A: Joint B:

Joint C   Joint D

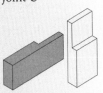
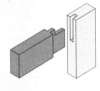

State the name of each joint. (4)

(b) State **two** methods of ensuring the frame is square. (2)

ANSWERS

ANSWERS 1

1. (a)White Pine, Red Pine or any other suitable softwood.
   (b)Mahogany, Meranti, Oak or any other suitable hardwood.
   (c)Joint A: Haunched Mortise and Tenon joint. Joint B: Dowel joint. Joint C: Butt joint.
   (d)A Haunched Mortise and Tenon joint was chosen due to it being the strongest joint out of the three joints.
2. (a)Cross-halving joint.
   (b)PVA glue.
3. Joint A: Corner-halving joint; Joint B: Mitre joint.
4. (a)Forstner bit or flat bit.
   (b)Pillar/pedestal drill.
   (c)Ensure scrap wood is placed underneath, drill at a slow pace.

5. (a)Marking gauge
   (b)Bevel edge chisel, Firmer chisel or Mortise chisel.
   (c)Smoothing plane or Jack plane.
6. (a)Stopped housing joint.
   (b)Corner rebate joint.
7. (a)Tool rest.
   (b)To adjust the height of the tool rest.
   (c)To secure the tool rest the to the bed of the lathe.
   (d)Skew chisel.
   (e)To protect the candle holder, to enhance the appearance of the candle holder.

ANSWERS 2

1. Any two from: available in large sheets, lightweight, strong, stable – will not warp/twist, quality finish, cost, durable and defect-free.
2. MDF or any other suitable manufactured board. Hardboard is unsuitable.
3. Two clear differences between the two manufactured boards. Multilayers in plywood/layer direction should be mentioned.
4. The shapes of each side will be identical, it's easier, it's accurate, it's quicker, can be used repeatedly.
5. Jig saw.
6. Safety goggles, dust extraction, workpiece secured to desk or held in bench vice, drill bit/saw blade secured in power tool, guard in place (if fitted with a guard), position of cable considered (if attached to cable). Any other valid safety precaution.
7. Drill hole in slot shape outline, slacken handle of coping saw, remove blade, place blade through the drilled hole, replace blade back onto frame, cut out slot shape.

8. A knock down fitting, a cross dowel, a barrel and bolt.
9. Quick and easy to assemble. Can be taken apart then reassembled.
10. Twist drill
11. Machine A: Pillar/Pedestal drill. Power tool B: Cordless drill. Hand tool C: Hand drill.
12. Any one from: Chuck key removed, chuck guard is down, workpiece is held securely, eye protection on, loose hair tied back. Any other suitable safety check.
13. Any two from: To protect the wood, to enhance the look, to seal it, to make it easier to clean, to prevent it from getting marked.
14. Glass paper and garnet paper.
15. Medium and fine.

ANSWERS 3

1. Red Pine, White Pine, Cedar or Larch.
2. Stain.
3. Tool A: Measuring tape, Tool B: Try square, Tool C: Marking knife, Tool D: Twist drill, Tool E: Bradawl, Tool F: Countersink rose, Tool G: Cross head screwdriver, Power tool H: Jig saw, Power tool I: Orbital sander, Power tool J: Corded drill.

4. Safety goggles, dust extraction, workpiece secured to desk or held in bench vice, drill bit/saw blade secured in power tool, guard in place (if fitted with a guard), position of cable considered (if attached to cable). Any other valid safety precaution.
5. Hole A: Countersink hole. Hole B: Clearance hole. Hole C: Pilot hole.
6. So that the head of the screw is flat/flush with the surface of the wood; so that the head of the screw doesn't stick out from the wood.
7. Hammer: Claw hammer. Nail: Round head nail.

ANSWERS 4

1. Corner rebate joint.
2. It's quite a weak joint, lack of strength, not strong enough.
3. Marking gauge.
4. A: Spur. B: Thumbscrew. C: Stem. D: Stock.
5. Oak, Beech, Mahogany, Meranti or any other suitable answer – not Balsa.
6. Softwood grows quicker than hardwood.
7. Multilayered, layers at 90°, or a sketch to indicate this.
8. Any two from: available in large sheets, lightweight, strong, stable – will not warp/twist, quality finish, cost, durable and defect-free.
9. A: Blade. B: Fence. C: Groove.

10. Tool A: Hand brace. Tool B: Forstner bit.
11. Any one from: Drill through into a piece of scrap wood or drill halfway through, then flip the wood and come in from the other side.
12. Dry clamping.
13. Removing pencil lines, wetting the wood to raise the grain.
14. Any two from: To protect the wood, to enhance the look, to seal it, to make it easier to clean, to prevent it from getting marked.
15. Any two from: a cutting list, the material to be used, the sizes of the parts, how it goes together.

ANSWERS 5

1. Mortise Gauge.
2. The distance between the spurs by adjusting the bass slide. The distance of the stock from the spurs by adjusting the thumbscrew.
3. Chisel A: Mortise chisel. Chisel B: Bevel edge chisel.
4. Ferrule.
5. To prevent the handle from cracking while being struck by a mallet.
6. A piece of tape or a pen mark can be applied to the chisel to mark the required depth of cut or a steel rule can be used to measure the depth of the mortise after each series of cuts.
7. The answer should relate to the chisel. Always cut away from the body. Keep both hands behind cutting surface, keep the work securely fixed, use a sharp chisel.

8. Tool A: Mallet. Tool B: Tenon saw. Tool C: Sawing board/bench hook.
9. Device A: Bench vice. Device B: G cramp/G clamp.
10. PVA glue.
11. Sash cramp.
12. Orbital sander, belt sander.
13. Smoothing plane, Jack plane
14. Screw: Round head screw. Fixing: Angle bracket.
15. Blockboard.
16. Mortise machine.

ANSWERS 6

1. Any suitable hardwood other than mahogany.
2. Belt sander or disc sander.
3. Flat bit.
4. One mark for any of the following: Drill through into a piece of scrap wood or drill halfway through then reverse the wood.
5. Knock down fixing/ KD fixings.
6. Part A: head stock. Part B: tool rest. Part C: bed. Part D: tail stock.
7. Any **one** from: it drives the wood, it turns the wood.
8. Revolving centre doesn't need lubrication, won't burn the end of the wood, reduces friction.

9. **Stage 2:** Using a hammer and a centre punch, create an indent in both ends to allow the centres to be located.
   Stage 3: Using a tenon saw, cut a groove to accommodate the forked centre.
   Stage 4: Using a smoothing plane, remove the corners of the blank to make the initial stage of turning a cylinder easier.
10. Outside callipers.
11. Gouge or scraper.
12. A skew chisel.
13. To achieve a good grip of the tool handle and to allow good leverage.
14. Removal of the tool rest, changing/increasing the lathe speed.

ANSWERS 7

1. Your answer should be a description of any two of the following:
   - Protect rainforests from deforestation
   - Faster speed of growth of softwood compared to hardwood
   - Lower levels of transport pollution for softwoods
   - Encourage sustainable forests
2. It is strong, it is stable, it is available in large sheets; environmental reasons.
3. (a)To allow the waste wood created by the centres to be trimmed off. Your answer should refer to waste wood being cut off.
   (b)To help hold the blank securely in place while the forked centre is turning it.
   (c)Parting chisel.
   (d)Skew chisel.
4. The speed could be increased.
5. (a)A template.
   (b)One mark for any of the following:
   - Accurate reproduction of complex shapes
   - Quick to mark out
   - Easy to mark out
   - Can be positioned on sheet material to economise cutting.

6. Spoke shave.
7. (a)Forstner bit, flat bit.
   (b)Twist drill.
   (c)Pillar/pedestal drill.
   (d)One mark for any of the following:
   - Guard down
   - Chuck key removed
   - Drill bit securely tightened in chuck
   - Drill bit held in chuck by shank
   - Workpiece to be drilled is held securely in place.
8. (a)Panel pin.
   (b)Tool A: Nail punch. Tool B: Cross-pein hammer.
   (c)A nail punch is used to drive the head of a nail or panel pin below the surface of the wood.
   (d)Pincers.
   (e)PVA glue.
9. Glass paper or garnet paper.
10. Any two from:
    - To enhance the look of the tray
    - To protect the wood
    - To prevent it from getting marked
    - To make the tray easier to clean.

ANSWERS 8

1. Stopped housing joint.
2. Sliding bevel.
3. (a)Handle.　　　　　(c)Tang.
   (b)Ferrule.　　　　 (d)Bevel edge chisel.
4. (a)Hand router.
   (b)Your answer should indicate slackening and tightening the depth stop screw and adjusting the height of blade either by measurement or to the gauge mark.
5. (a)G-cramp.
   (b)By placing a piece of scrap wood between the cramp and the surface of the side of the shoe rack.
6. Coping saw.
7. (a)Red pine, white pine or any other suitable softwood.
   (b)Any **two** from:
   - Scale used
   - Pictorial drawings
   - Orthographic drawings
   - Construction methods
   - Different views
   - The overall sizes of the shoe rack.

8. (a)Countersink screw.
   (b)So that the head of the screw is flush/flat with the surface of the wood.
   (c)Cross head screwdriver.
   (d)Bradawl.
   (e)A bradawl is a hand tool used to make pilot holes in wood for small screws.
9. (a)The assembled shoe rack is held together with sash cramps but **without the glue.**
   (b)Sash cramp.
   (c)• The back jaw can be moved into the rough position then the locking pin placed in position.
   • Tommy bar can be rotated to tighten or slacken the cramp.
10. (a)Any valid method, for example:
    - Removing pencils marks
    - Raising the grain/wetting the wood.
    (b)Description of applying varnish using a brush, cloth or spray.

ANSWERS 9

1. (a)Veneered chipboard, veneered MDF.
   (b)Dowel joint
   (c)Any one of the following:
   - using masking tape or a mark on the drill bit
   - using the depth stop on the pillar drill
   - adjust the height of table on the pillar drill.
2. (a)Any two from the following:
   - steel rule
   - try square
   - mortise gauge
   - marking knife.
   (b)The adhesive will need to withstand the wet conditions outside from rainwater and the water used to water the plants.
   (c)Block plane.　　　　(d)Plywood.
3. (a)Glass paper, garnet paper.　　(b)Band cramp.

4. (a)It increases the sustainability of the hardwood.
   (b)Oak.
   (c)Forstner bit, flat bit.
   (d)Any two from:
   - to enhance the look of it/ the grain
   - to make it easier to clean
   - to protect the wood
   - to prevent it from getting marked.
5. (a)Any three answers correct for 1 mark. All five answers correct for 2 marks.
   A: Rail, B: 2, C: 175, D: 40, E: 16.
   (b)Millimetres.
   (c)Red Pine, White Pine, Cedar, Larch.
   (d)Mitre cramp.

ANSWERS 10

1. (a)Any two from the following:
   - full face visor
   - goggles
   - dust protection/face mask
   - safety specs.
   (b)Forked centre/butterfly centre and revolving centre or dead centre.
   (c)Decent sketch of the blade of a gouge.
   (d)Jack plane, plane.
   (e)To change the angle of the blade. Level/straighten the blade.
   (f) To lower or raise the blade. Change the depth of cut.
2. (a)Cordless screwdriver, cordless drill.
   (b)Head stock.
   (c)Increase the speed of the wood lathe.

   (d)It's a non-toxic finish which is suitable for a workpiece that will come into contact with food.
3. (a)(i) Corner rebate (ii) Mitre joint.
   (b)Marking gauge.
   (c)Slacken the thumb screw. Set the distance from the stock to the front of the spur to 8 mm. Tighten the thumb screw and check the size.
   (d)Combination plane.
4. (a)Joint A: Corner bridle. Joint B: Haunched mortise and tenon. Joint C: Corner halving. Joint D: Butt joint.
   (b)Use a try square, measure across the diagonals to check they are equal.

Abrasive – A substance or material capable of polishing or cleaning a hard surface by rubbing or grinding.

Adhesive – A substance, such as glue, used for sticking objects or material together.

Blind hole – A blind hole refers to a hole that has been drilled to a specified depth without breaking through to the other side of the material.

Burr – After the sharpening angle on a chisel has been honed, you will notice a fine burr has been produced on the underside of the blade.

Chopping – Chopping refers to removing large areas of waste wood by driving a chisel with blows from a mallet. Chopping is mainly used when creating joints.

Cross cut – A crosscut saw is used to make a cut at a right angle to the direction of the grain of the workpiece. When you cut across the grain this is known as a crosscut.

Cutting list – A cutting list is an integral part of any working drawing. It includes an accurate, itemised list of all the individual parts that are required in the manufacture of a product.

Datum edge – When marking out on wood, measurements should be taken from a datum. A datum edge is a flat or straight edge from which all measurements should be taken, otherwise you're in danger of making cumulative errors.

Depth stop – A depth stop is set to determine the depth of cut made by a blade, chisel or drill bit.

Dry cramping – Dry cramping is when you cramp up your model without applying any glue. The purpose of dry cramping is to make sure that all the joints fit together properly and there are no mistakes before applying the glue.

Durability – This is the ability of a material to withstand wear, especially as a result of weathering.

Ease of working – How a material behaves when worked by hand or machine tools.

Flat-pack furniture – A type of self-assembly furniture that is commonly made from manufactured board and joined using various mechanical fixings known as knock down fixings.

FSC – The Forestry Stewardship Council (FSC) is an international organisation that promotes the sustainable management of forests, and certifies that products such as wood, paper and card that carry the FSC logo are produced from trees that come from responsibly managed forests.

Gloss finish – A gloss finish is a shiny smooth surface.

Groove – In woodworking, a groove is a slot or channel cut into a piece of wood which runs parallel to the grain.

Hardness – The ability of a material to resist wear, scratching and indentation.

Hardwood – Hardwoods come from broadleaved deciduous trees which lose their leaves in autumn and grow in the familiar mushroom shape. Some common hardwoods are oak, mahogany and beech.

Machine vice – A vice used to hold small workpieces firmly in place whilst using a pillar drill.

Matt finish – A matt finish will leave a dull surface.

Muntin – The name given to the dividing or centre vertical member (stile) within a basic flat frame construction.

Paring – Paring refers to the removal of small shavings using only hand pressure. Paring is often used where intricate woodworking is needed, such as finishing a joint to achieve a tight fit.

PVA glue – PVA (polyvinyl-acetate) glue is a thick, white water-based glue. Unlike superglue, which has a very short setting time, PVA will take around 3–4 hours to dry and set to a strong, permanent joint.

Rail – The name given to the horizontal members within a basic flat frame construction.

Recycling – The term recycling a material means that at the end of the material's life, it is broken down then processed into a new, usable product.

Reuse – The term reuse is often confused with recycle, but the main difference with reuse is that you're not breaking the product down: what you are effectively doing is taking an item and using it again, but perhaps for a different purpose.

Ripping – A rip saw is used to make a cut parallel to the direction of the grain of the workpiece. When you cut along the grain, this is known as ripping.

Scale – Working drawings are drawn to scale and the scale used will be indicated on the drawing. The scale used by the designer will depend on either the actual size of the original product or the level of detail that is required to be shown. For example, if the product has been drawn to its actual size, it has been drawn to a scale of 1:1; however, if the designer needed to show an intricate detail of a part, they may increase the scale used to perhaps 2:1, which would make the drawing twice as large as the actual size.

Silk finish – A silk finish, also known as satin finish, is a slightly dull shiny surface.

Softwood – Softwoods come from coniferous (cone-bearing) trees which are sometimes known as evergreens. They normally grow tall and slender and keep their needle-like leaves throughout the year. Common softwoods are pine, cedar and larch.

Stile – The name given to the vertical members within a basic flat frame construction.

Strength – The strength of wood is determined by its density. This is the wood's ability to withstand a force without breaking or bending.

Template – A marking out aid created for when you need to mark out the same shape a number of times, particularly irregular shapes. The template is placed on the material to be cut out then drawn around. You can make a template out of any thin scrap material such as card, plywood, aluminium or plastic. The type of material chosen for a template is determined by the number of times it is to be used.

Third angle projection – The 3rd angle projection symbol is used to indicate the order in which the different views of an object are laid out in an orthographic drawing. For example, the front view, called the elevation, is placed under the plan view, which is the view of the object looking at it from above.

Tolerance – The permissible amount of variation to the size given in a working drawing or a gap between a joint. The tolerance that you will be expected to work to for National 5 is ± 1 mm (plus or minus 1 mm).

Torque – Torque is a measure of how much a force acting on an object causes that object to rotate.

TPI – A common measurement of the number of teeth residing in any one-inch (25 mm) length of the saw blade. As a rule, a saw with a higher number of TPI gives a finer finish than larger toothed handsaws with a much smaller number of TPI (Teeth Per Inch).

Visor – A visor offers full face protection and is mainly recommended for use when working on a woodturning lathe.

Woodturning lathe – A woodturning lathe is a fixed machine used to turn cylindrical shapes from a solid piece of wood using a variety of tools and chisels.

Working drawing – The primary purpose of a working drawing is to provide you with all the information you need to make all the component parts, and to show you how each of those individual parts will be joined together. Working drawings tend to be produced by designers, architects or CAD technicians and then passed on to other professionals such as engineers, builders and joiners to read and work from. With this in mind, they have to present the information in such a way that it eliminates confusion.